A guide to successful dissertation study

A guide to successful dissertation study for students of the built environment

Second edition

Dr Gary D. Holt

Published by
The Built Environment Research Unit
School of Engineering and the Built Environment
University of Wolverhampton
West Midlands
WV1 1SB
United Kingdom

First published 1997

Second edition 1998 ISBN: 1-902010-01-9

Typeset by the author
Printed by University of Wolverhampton Print Services

Acknowledgements

First and foremost, I extend a big thank you to my wife Lynn and two children Mark and Rod. They have always supported me fully throughout all of my academic endeavours. *I dedicate this book to them.*

Gratitude is also expressed to my academic colleagues, particularly:

Professor Frank Harris, who taught me self belief.
Dr Paul Olomolaiye, for his assiduous encouragement.
Dr John Dews, for helping to germinate the original idea for this book.
Dr Dave Halsey, for writing the section on physical experiments.
Dr Les Ruddock of Salford University, for his kind help and advice.
Mr David Proverbs for proof reading the second edition.

Finally, I acknowledge all of my Built Environment research colleagues past and present, the world over. Many of the scenarios and examples cited in this text, are based on their (our) combined experiences.

Education is what remains when what has been learned is forgotten (Anon).

Gary Holt
March 1998

The Author

Gary D. Holt O.N.C, H.N.C, B.Sc (Hons), Ph.D, F.C.I.O.B., M.A.S.C.E (USA), F.F.B.

Reader in Construction Management within the Built Environment Research Unit at the University of Wolverhampton, UK. Dr Holt is dissertation co-ordinator for all Built Environment undergraduates within the University and has successfully supervised numerous undergraduate, MSc and PhD built environment dissertation and research programmes. Has undertaken consultancy and research in collaboration with industry and research-funding bodies such as The Leverhulme Trust and the Engineering and Physical Sciences Research Council, of the United Kingdom. His work has been broadly disseminated through international construction conferences and journals including: *Building and Environment; Construction Management and Economics; Building Research and Information; Construction Procurement; Engineering, Construction and Architectural Management; The International Journal of Project Management; The American Society of Civil Engineers; and Proceedings of The Institution of Civil Engineers.* Has provided technical illustrations for text books, authored one previous text book and is currently co-authoring another two books reporting his most recent research findings.

Contents

Chapter four
Third component: the end

Chapter five
Concluding tasks and thoughts

Chapter six
Summary of tips

References and bibliography

Appendices

Subject index

List of figures

List of tables

Appendices

Introduction

This introduction:

- outlines the aims of this book
- explains how to use this book
- provides an overview of the chapters

This book explains how to successfully research a subject and present the findings of that research, in the form of a dissertation.

The book is written in a built environment context; this is because it is aimed primarily at undergraduate dissertation students of the built environment. However, despite the book's specific subject bias, the majority of methods and guidance cited within it are equally useful to all dissertation students, regardless of subject. Furthermore, the book is designed to provide a basic foundation for any level of research study e.g. Masters', MPhil and to a limited extent, PhD. Indeed, it should be noted that the fundamental concepts upon which the book is based (logical task structure, careful planning, adequate researching of information and good presentation), hold potential benefit to *all* students, pursuing *any* written assignment work.

As will become clear, a dissertation and a thesis are two quite different pieces of work; even though both are based upon research. Because of this, each is referred to separately throughout this book. However, in more general terms most of the principles and practices involved in the successful compilation of either, are identical.

For the sake of readability therefore, unless otherwise indicated the reader is asked to perceive the use of the word dissertation within the following narrative, as applying equally to thesis.

It is generally accepted that a formal text should avoid using the first-person (e.g. "I was . ." or, "My experience is . . ."). This maxim can equally apply to a dissertation (more on that in chapter five) or a book such as this one. However, I plead guilty of writing in the first person in this narrative because:

- O   excessive use of passive text can seem uncomfortable and artificial (Kirkman, 1995); and
- O   I am attempting to 'talk to you' via this text and occasional use of the first-person better helps me achieve this.

Aims of this book

This book has one fundamental aim:

<u>To serve as a good practice guide</u> for students having to undertake a dissertation or thesis.

If you are such a student, then proper use of this book will help you compile a *successful* piece of work. In this context, the word successful is important. Personal experience has demonstrated to me that a significant number of students fail to capitalise on their dissertation study. On the contrary, many find it a tedious affair. Their dissertation is 'just another obstacle' that must be overcome to achieve an academic award. This 'failure to capitalise' is often because students do not fully appreciate: what a dissertation really is; why the dissertation is being compiled; what the correct approach to dissertation study should be; and perhaps most importantly, the potential impact that dissertation study can have on an individual.

A successful dissertation is founded upon sound academic principles. It will have a clearly communicated objective, and this objective will be satisfied using research methods that have rigour in them. A successful dissertation student will enjoy the experience and learn a lot from it. The dissertation will achieve a 'good' grade and contribute significantly (or in its entirety) to an academic award. A successful dissertation can amongst other things: contribute towards a higher classification of degree; develop individual character in ways that may not have at first been anticipated (e.g. the ability to 'see a problem through'); serve as a valuable keepsake representing an important milestone in one's life; mirror the ability and character of an individual; contribute towards a successful job interview; and so on. Hence, the importance of compiling a successful dissertation becomes clear. To put it another way, the potential adverse effects of *not* compiling a successful dissertation are greater in magnitude than a student may at first appreciate.

> TIP: A good dissertation has a clearly communicated objective(s).

At this juncture, I should point out that this book purposely ignores certain aspects of dissertation study. First, it will not suggest the best subject area to research nor identify what needs researching. To attempt that would be near impossible. Research is by nature a 'moving target' with existing problems constantly being solved or better understood whilst simultaneously, new challenges are forever being identified. Research is about challenging traditional wisdom (e.g. traditionally we have always done it like this; but could we do it better?) and investigation of 'hot' or topical issues. Bear this in mind when choosing a research subject. The book does offer common sense guidance towards making a rational subject choice, in chapter one.

Second, the book does not give specific advice as to exactly which research method should be applied to a given situation, or, attempt to identify exactly what type of model needs to be developed for a specific problem. There are fundamental ground rules, but each dissertation problem (or investigation) setting will be unique in terms of time scale, resources, researcher ability, objectives and so forth. Likewise, the research solution for a given setting will be unique also.

Finally, this book does not offer detailed advice regarding the finer aspects of writing style. It would be pointless my adding to the multitude of books already available on that subject (see chapter five). If you do find it difficult to write clearly and coherently there is only one solution: practice! In the meantime, be sure to edit your work many times over (see chapter five) and liaise closely with your dissertation supervisor(s).

So what then *does* this book offer?

It provides step-by-step guidance through the dissertation experience. Advice is given as to avoiding the pitfalls that await all students about to embark on a dissertation, as a means of highlighting ways of working *effectively*. In this respect consider the following aphorism: "don't tell me what you've done, tell me what you've achieved". The difference between being efficient and effective is important:

> *A dissertation student suffering from 'headless-chicken-syndrome' will work a lot harder and burn more midnight oil, than the student with a well defined plan, a realistic time scale, clear objectives and a full understanding of how those objectives are to be satisfied.*

That is, upon completion of their dissertation the 'headless-chicken' student will have done a lot, but will have achieved much less. The organised student will have been effective and *achieved* a lot. The organised student will have achieved a successful dissertation.

> TIP: Be effective in what you do. Very often, to be efficient is not in itself enough.

This book considers a dissertation with respect to built environment research generally. It offers broad advice towards topic choice and selection of research methodology. It explains how to plan, execute and control the dissertation task. It describes how to structure the entire dissertation exercise and explains the structure of a good dissertation in itself. This book can be used to simply achieve an overview of dissertation study and / or, be consulted on an ad-hoc basis for guidance on specific aspects of the subject.

One further item deserves mention. Learning can and should be enjoyable. A student who believes that to be successful in academic endeavour involves a totally straight-laced disposition is, for my part, misguided. Your dissertation learning experience can be enjoyable so please, do not lose your ability to smile. A sense of humour can be the best defence against stress, frustration and pressure. Believe me, if you are to pursue your dissertation properly you will certainly experience all of these emotions!

How to use this book

Before writing this book, I assumed that the majority of readers would not consider reading it until they were just about to begin, or more probably had begun, their dissertation. Typically, this will be the final year of study for undergraduate students or final semester of study for postgraduates. In the case of a research thesis, the student is probably about to commence a higher degree by way of a fixed term of research, (e.g. usually three years full time for a PhD).

Because of these scenarios time is the student's biggest enemy. Therefore, a concise text was my aim. However, the more concise a text then the greater is potential for omitting certain aspects of the subject. For this reason references are cited throughout the book, using the Harvard method (i.e. author and date of publication: see chapter two later).

Full bibliographic details of each reference are listed at the rear of the book along with other complementary reading. This provision will allow a student to follow up particular (specific) areas of interest in greater detail as appropriate.

First, it is recommended that chapter one is read carefully and comprehensively. Understanding the fundamentals is an essential prerequisite to subsequent progression. Also, appreciation of the 'three component' concept (beginning, middle, end) is vital in order to produce any successful piece of written work.

Following this, chapters two, three and four may be speed-read to gain an appreciation of these three basic components (and hence stages in production) of a dissertation. Speed-reading means reading the text so as to comprehend it, but quickly! This is a skill that has to be learned for research in order that voluminous amounts of information can be 'scanned'. A useful tip is to initially read the first and last sentences (only) of every paragraph. Then, having obtained a 'flavour' of the text, particular sections of relevance or interest may be re-read more slowly.

> TIP: Learn to speed-read in order that you may scan large volumes of text quickly. Only relevant items of text need to be read slowly.

Once you have started to write your dissertation then chapter two *The beginning* may be re-read in a more meaningful manner. The advice offered may then be acted upon almost simultaneously.

As your dissertation progresses, chapters three *The middle* and four *The end* will logically fall into place and should also therefore, be re-read and understood fully.

Chapter five may be speed-read early on, paying particular attention to the section: *Pitfalls to avoid*. A more meaningful digestion of chapter five should be performed when the dissertation is all but completed. This is when you will need to consider editing the text, making corrections and certain aspects of writing style. The latter items must be addressed prior to submission of the work to the examiner(s) and where applicable, the oral examination (the viva-voce). Figure 1.0. shows graphically, the recommended way to use this book.

Obviously, the above advice is indicative. Ideally, this book will be read well before a dissertation is commenced. That way, a student will have more time to assimilate its contents.

Figure 1. How to use this book

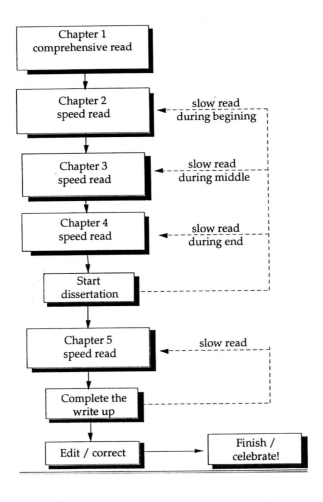

Therein lies another maxim: being armed with the necessary information before diving head first into any venture, makes for better planning and technique.

Overview of the chapters

Chapter one

This deals with fundamental issues. The nature of built environment research is outlined and the differences between a dissertation and a thesis are confirmed. The need to identify the rules and to write for your principal reader are discussed, as are the problems surrounding topic choice, planning the dissertation task, and deciding structure and strategy. The 'three component' concept is introduced at the end of the chapter.

Chapter two

The required format of a dissertation and other 'preliminary' issues are discussed here. Specific advice is also given on writing the introductory text, effectively performing a literature search, referencing the narrative correctly and identifying (and communicating) meaningful dissertation objectives.

Chapter three

This deals with the middle component of a dissertation. Choice of research methodology with respect to achieving desired objectives, along with sampling, surveys and experiments are briefly explored. The problems of logically analysing research data and clearly presenting findings from that analysis, are also discussed. This is the biggest chapter of the book and reflects that this is the most difficult and arguably important, part of a dissertation.

Chapter four

The abstraction and presentation of meaningful conclusions are the subjects of this chapter. The correct way to list references, the compilation of a bibliography and the use of appendices and a glossary are also explained.

Chapter five

This describes how to edit and correct the dissertation and looks at certain aspects of writing style. Pitfalls to avoid during the dissertation experience are highlighted, in particular, based on a small survey of dissertation supervisors. Finally, advice is offered to prepare a student who is required to sit for an oral examination (a viva-voce).

Chapter six

A summary of all the tips given throughout this entire book are collated here.

References and bibliography

A list of references cited within the text, along with bibliographic details of other complementary reading is provided.

Appendices

Supplementary information to the text is provided here.

Subject index

A comprehensive list of subject keywords and respective page numbers.

Chapter one
The fundamentals

This chapter explains the following points:

- ❑ what research is about
- ❑ what a dissertation is
- ❑ what a thesis is
- ❑ how to choose a dissertation topic
- ❑ how rules govern dissertation study
- ❑ the importance of writing for your principal reader
- ❑ how to plan your dissertation study
- ❑ what is meant by the 'three component' concept

The man who moves a mountain begins by carrying away small stones (Confucius 551-479 B.C.)

Introduction

As any student of the built environment will know all construction must be built on good foundations. Poor foundations lead to subsequent settlement and construction damage, or in the extreme, total construction failure. In either case, the resulting construction will be sub-standard. How apt then to use this as an analogy for the purpose of this chapter. If you understand the fundamental concepts of dissertation study then you start with a good foundation. That way, you lessen the probability that your dissertation will suffer 'damage', or in the extreme, will fail altogether.

What is research?

Evolution brings about changes that can yield benefits, for example, the ability of a species to cope with a changing environment. Some of the earliest living things were just a single cell. Some of these cells were misfits and soon died whilst others survived. Through heredity the survivors passed their more superior characteristics to descendants and hence, from one 'superior' cell came another. Eventually, single celled organisms gave rise to more complex plants and animals consisting of many cells. This is a perfect example of evolutionary improvement. However, the biggest drawback of the evolutionary process is that it takes an inordinate amount of time, in the latter example over 3000 million years! In relative terms our own life spans are extremely short, we cannot afford to simply sit back and wait for benefits to 'evolve'.

Albeit an analogy, the above perfectly puts research into perspective. If we can 'model' real life situations and observe the effects of applying change to what is accepted as the norm (i.e. 'traditional wisdom'), then any improvements stemming from such intervention can be adopted by the species as a whole. This is exactly what built environment research attempts to achieve, i.e. take a given problem setting (the norm); model that setting (can be a physical model such as a scale building for wind tunnel testing or a symbolic model such as a computer mock up); introduce change (normally what we have postulated will be improvement); and observe the effects of such change. Where improvement is identified, that is, the model is superior to the norm, then all other things being equal (e.g. it is financially viable) this improvement may be adopted by the industry -see Figure 1.1.

This scenario is typical of *applied* research, i.e. that which attempts to resolve practical problems or improve on traditional thinking. Consider for a moment the increasing use of plastic pipework and fittings for building services. Unlike their steel or copper counterparts, plastic is corrosion resistant, flexible, easy to joint, and resistant to the effects of expansion from freezing. Such advances in materials technology are a direct result of applied research.

Figure 1.1. Applied construction research

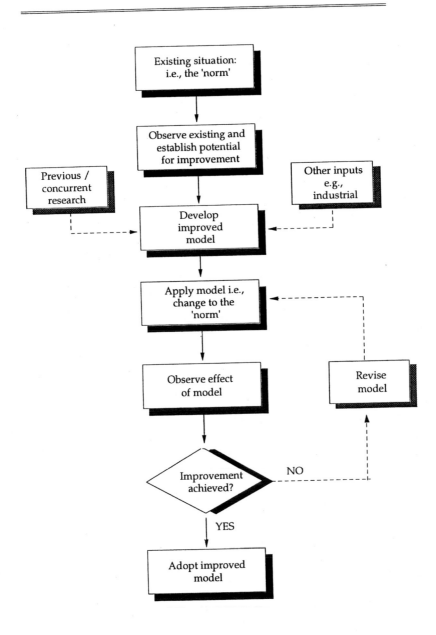

One of the principal organisations for conducting applied research in the UK construction sector, is the Building Research Establishment (BRE) whose headquarters are at Garston, Watford. An excellent summary of BRE activities will be found on the Internet at: www.bre.co.uk.

A dissertation student will do well at this point to note also that the BRE produce information digests, technical papers, defect action sheets, books, reports, slide packs and videos. These are valuable sources of information and data for all studying the built environment, or who are performing construction research. (A comprehensive list of information sources is given in chapter 2: *The introductory text and literature review*).

Another facet of applied built environment research, is by way of postgraduate students undertaking research for a higher degree such as Doctor of Philosophy (PhD). The majority of these degrees are conducted within Universities, often in collaboration with industry. Some PhDs are pursued in an industrial setting but with an appropriate academic input. Either way, the fundamental ethos of applied research remains.

An alternative classification is *pure* research. This tends to address more theoretical issues in an attempt to placate a thirst for knowledge (Holt, 1994) and might be perceived as being more academic (vis-à-vis industrial or commercial in nature) than applied research. For example, pure research could measure opinion or perception concerning a particular subject, such as: how do construction clients perceive their role in the procurement process? Notwithstanding its theoretical bias it would be unfair to consider pure research as being less useful than applied research. Indeed, a comprehensive research programme will encompass both applied and pure to some extent. In the context of this book, pure research is most often a feature of undergraduate dissertations.

Having identified the rudiments of built environment research, we will now consider in more detail the differences between a dissertation and a thesis.

The dissertation

There are two broad categories here: first degree dissertations and postgraduate dissertations.

A first degree (undergraduate) dissertation

This is normally that extra component of academic study that converts an unclassified, or pass, or ordinary degree (e.g. BSc) into a classified honours degree e.g. BSc (Hons) 1st class. It is a written presentation of a subject (Barrass, 1978); obviously, a subject intrinsically linked to the theme of that degree being studied. It provides a student opportunity to use intellectual and practical skills and to demonstrate initiative, creativity and analytical adequacy (Anon, 1995a). The learning outcomes for a first degree dissertation will include the abilities to:

- plan and execute a programme of work within a given time schedule;
- undertake a detailed and comprehensive literature search;
- critically analyse and draw up reasoned conclusions based on an existing knowledge base;
- appreciate how to research a given problem setting; and
- present a logical, coherent written report of the research (the dissertation) and defend such report orally, if requested.

In short, a first degree dissertation is an in-depth study of a specific aspect of the degree subject studied. The better first degree dissertations will encompass an element of pure research such as measurement of opinion, or detailed observation of current practice / procedures. This is very often achieved through structured survey (discussed in chapter 3). If this measurement / observation (etc.) is properly designed and executed, then analysis of the accumulated data is possible, which in turn facilitates abstraction of meaningful conclusions and possibly, recommendations. These elements of pure research (seek information, analyse information, proffer conclusions) are an essential and important requisite to a good dissertation. A first degree dissertation is more than simply a comprehensive assignment[1].

Postgraduate dissertations

These may be classified as either forming part of predetermined formal study, such as a modular MSc and those which are the result of study for a higher degree by way of research e.g. Master of Philosophy (MPhil).

The former will be somewhat similar in structure to a first degree dissertation. However, a postgraduate dissertation is a higher level of academic study and this should be reflected in the quality and usefulness of the work (essentially research) undertaken. Postgraduate dissertations should encompass a <u>critical discussion</u> of existing literature on the chosen topic, and an in-depth element of <u>originality</u>. The original element will normally be achieved through well designed and implemented pure research (but applied research is not excluded), the data from which should be comprehensively and where possible, quantitatively analysed to produce meaningful results and firm conclusions and recommendations. It should be noted at this point that to produce good quality academic work, there is no substitute for originality based on sound research and careful, logical reasoning.

TIP: Good academic work (particularly that which is research based) exhibits a high content of originality.

An MPhil dissertation results from a programme of pure or applied research. It reflects the effort of a student who: ". . . having critically investigated and evaluated an approved topic and demonstrated an understanding of research methods appropriate to the chosen field, has presented and defended a dissertation to the satisfaction of the examiners" (Anon, 1995b). This can therefore be classified as a true research degree dissertation. Both MSc and MPhil dissertations are based upon training in the problems and methods of scientific investigation, using independent research.

---

[1]Here, the word assignment is used in its academic context.

My own 'acid test' for a good first degree, Masters or research dissertation is this: Can a robust research paper (i.e. a technical paper suitable for presentation to a refereed academic journal) be abstracted from it? Failure by a student to have adequately performed one of the essentials (literature review, originality, meaningful analysis, logical conclusions) will render this impossible. However, the converse holds true.

The thesis

A thesis accurately reports the results of a higher degree research programme and in doing so makes a contribution to knowledge (typically this is the PhD). It is useful at this point to consider the following definitions:

Hypothesis: a suggested explanation for a group of facts or phenomena either accepted as a basis for further verification (known as a working hypothesis) or, accepted as likely to be true;

Thesis: a dissertation resulting from original research, or a doctrine maintained in an argument (Collins English Dictionary).

We can establish therefore, that a thesis is a form of dissertation, reporting original (normally applied but not excluding pure) research. It is indeed a form of argument. That is, it reflects the hypothesis originated and subsequently corroborated by the researcher, (in successful theses!) concerning the subject investigated.

This is what sets a thesis apart from a first degree or postgraduate dissertation: a thesis represents an *original* argument put forward by the research student and goes on to substantiate that argument. Hence, in achieving this the researcher makes a contribution to knowledge: "The PhD shall be awarded to a candidate who, having critically investigated and evaluated an approved topic resulting in an independent and original contribution to knowledge and demonstrated an understanding of research methods applicable to the chosen field, has presented and

16

defended a thesis to the satisfaction of the examiners" (Anon, 1995b). This is a mouthful, but it certainly confirms what a thesis is!

So, to reflect on the former definitions: a *working hypothesis* is firstly developed and the researcher goes on to substantiate or validate that hypothesis, which is ultimately presented in written form via the *thesis*. My acid test for a good thesis is that it will provide scope for *several* academic papers to be abstracted from it. The contrast between dissertation and thesis is now clear. A dissertation is an in-depth study of a subject i.e. it is based on existing knowledge, whereas a thesis must contribute to knowledge.

Choosing a dissertation topic

Where free choice is available, then appropriate choice of topic is perhaps the most important decision to be made in the entire dissertation programme.

> TIP: The appropriate choice of subject is a prerequisite to successful dissertations.

However, this decision is not an easy one; the difficulties associated with choosing a suitable subject have long been recognised (Parsons, 1973). In the case of many PhDs very often the programme of research (timescale and subject) has already been established prior to a student commencing the work. That is, a researcher is often employed specifically to execute a predetermined project. In such cases there will obviously be limited flexibility regarding topic choice. At this point it is worth mention that in such cases of postgraduate research, the student should be well versed in the subject area. My own experience has witnessed an individual qualified in medicine seeking to undertake research in construction management. Although the fundamental aspects of all research are common, one must question the compatibility of some (i.e. the latter two) disciplines!

Regarding undergraduate (e.g. BSc) and postgraduate (e.g. MSc) dissertations, the choice of topic is, normally, entirely at the student's discretion. In such circumstances I cannot advocate a definitive method of topic choice but rather, direct the student to the following considerations; each now briefly discussed in turn. Note that the list is not exhaustive; other considerations may impact the decision dependent on the setting.

Student ability / knowledge of the subject

As highlighted above, it is sensible that the chosen topic is within the student's ability or more specifically, that it falls within the domain of the subjects that have been studied at first or postgraduate degree level. To choose a subject that lies beyond the remit of your own 'specialism' introduces an (unnecessary) extra element of difficulty. If a particular subject was investigated at first degree level then very often this can serve as a 'springboard' for a higher degree dissertation. But beware, the latter must be original over-and-above the former; do not attempt to include work for a higher degree that has previously been submitted elsewhere. (There is a slight exception to this; see *Declaration* chapter two).

Area of student's interest

It goes without saying that the topic chosen should appeal to the student. This is so that enthusiasm can be maintained. You must be interested in your dissertation subject. Correlation exists between things that we are good at and things we enjoy doing. To demonstrate this point consider it the opposite way around. If you think for a moment about the things you dislike doing; chances are these will also be things that you are less able at!

Availability of information

In the case of a dissertation there is little sense in choosing a topic for which very little information exists, or for which information is quite inaccessible. (In contrast, a thesis will by its nature deal with a subject for which existing information may be scarce). Such a dissertation will duly grind to a halt.

Similarly, a lack of tangible information or research data makes for a text of very little substance. If in doubt, it may be worthwhile making some preliminary enquiries as to the availability of information for the potential topic and then carefully assessing the proposal with your supervisor. If you do not have a supervisor assigned to you at this stage, then discuss your proposal with someone who has research / supervision experience. As an example, I recall an undergraduate who wanted to investigate the use and conservation of energy in industrial buildings. The student identified a company that took this subject very seriously, and which had put in place a formal energy management procedure for all of its properties. The student selected this company for a case study; the entire dissertation was to be written around it. Not until the dissertation was well under way did the student find that the company would not participate in any way; so the dissertation came to an abrupt stop. (Another important point is this, had the student liaised earlier and more frequently with his supervisor then he could have been advised accordingly).

> TIP: Discuss your proposals with your supervisor at an early stage. If the proposals are flawed you can then be advised accordingly.

Amount of research required

What amount of research will need to be undertaken as to enable a student to adequately pursue their chosen topic? (and thus produce a meaningful piece of work). Most importantly, is this volume of research realistically possible within the available time scale? For example, to travel around the country and collect taped interview data (see *Structured interviews* chapter three), requires a lot of time and may be too demanding for a part time student in full time employment. If you feel that the required volume (method) of research is unmanageable, do not take the risk, either choose another topic or revise your research methodology.

Method of data collection required

What method of data or information collection will you require? For example, there is little point in studying operatives' productivity if inter-personal communication, time study and activity sampling skills are not your better traits. Likewise, a laboratory experiment that will only yield data at two-monthly intervals, is of little real use to a student with only a few months available to complete their research and write a dissertation based on it.

Degree of objectivity required

How quantitative does the treatment or analysis of your chosen topic need to be? Data requiring extensive, advanced statistical analyses are of little use to a student whose numeric ability leaves something to be desired. Alternatively, many topics may be adequately investigated at undergraduate level using a qualitative, less numeric, approach. This is where you need to consider several things jointly: your subject, your principal objective, the nature of your data and suitable method(s) of data analysis.

The employer's role

In the case of an employed part time student; has your present employer expressed a preference for your dissertation subject or perhaps requested an input to it? (You will earn more support from your employer if the subject is of interest or potential benefit to them). If you are a full time student, then will the subject enhance your future employment prospects? A dissertation can certainly add to your personal employment 'portfolio' and after all, why take on such a comprehensive programme of study if not in part to improve future employment prospects? Further, if your dissertation learns you a lot about your vocation (specialism) you will be better informed and hence more employable in that respect.

> TIP: Remember that your dissertation can play a significant role in your present and future employment prospects!

Collaboration required / available

Will the topic require industrial or commercial collaboration? For example, to help develop / validate a model, or for data collection or case study purposes. If this is so, be sure such collaborating organisations can be identified and more importantly, are willing to participate in your project. (Refer the real life example under *availability of information* above). It is also worth remembering that adverse macroeconomic forces can impart pressures upon potential industrial 'partners' or contributors, making spare resources (including their time) particularly precious.

Who are the supervisor(s) / examiner(s) ?

Is there a suitable supervisor for your proposed topic e.g. qualified in the subject area? Alternatively, will the chosen topic mean that the most suitable supervisor is one with whom you have a personality clash? Better to try a different subject (or supervisor if possible!) rather than risk a period of potential conflict or disagreement throughout the dissertation programme.

> TIP: Successful dissertations rely in part, on a good student / supervisor relationship.

The above list of considerations regarding topic choice is indicative only, as with so many other aspects of dissertation study such considerations are a function of individual setting. However, the list does consider many essential points and if used as a basis for thought, will help direct a student towards sensible subject choice.

Do not try and be too specific regarding topic at the outset. This is because until the literature search (chapter two) is well under way, you cannot be entirely certain as to which direction the research will *need* to go. For example, upon reading the literature it might become apparent that some aspects of the chosen subject have already been comprehensively researched, thereby 'stone walling' a route originally intended. Conversely, it may unfold that other aspects of the topic are yearning for further research and hence, potentially make for a particularly interesting piece of work. Aim to initially select a 'broad' subject area then concentrate on one specific aspect of it, as the literature search and hence your thinking on the subject, progresses.

Sharp and Howard (1996) suggest that the following list of factors should be considered in assessing the feasibility of a proposed research. It follows therefore that they also impact upon subject choice:

O   accessibility of information;
O   opportunity for particular research design (is subject compatible with the proposed research methodology and vice-versa?);
O   time considerations;
O   technical skills required of the student;
O   financial support required / available; and
O   risk (what is the potential for satisfactory completion?).

Identifying the rules and writing for the principal reader

Two more fundamentals should be considered early on. What are the rules governing the dissertation and who is to be the principal reader? I have linked these items together because the latter will to a certain extent influence the former.

Let us consider the first point. Obviously, there will be rules governing a dissertation. These may be formal, such as a fixed hand-in date for the finished product (after which time the work will be penalised for being late); or informal, such as don't bother your supervisor on Wednesday mornings! Keep within the rules and the task will be easier than if you decide to try and ignore them. Because every dissertation is compiled under differing circumstances e.g. subject, mode of study, place of study, then the rules will vary. Notwithstanding this, some common rules will now be discussed.

There should exist a formal document describing the rules and guidelines governing your dissertation. This will be labelled a 'module guide', 'project guide', 'dissertation guide or manual' or 'rules for the award of. . .' etc. It is of course difficult for me to generalise concerning document content but amongst other things it will probably contain information on: policy and guidelines; timescale and completion deadlines; required presentation and format; registration procedure for the academic award; supervision; grievance procedure; and examinations.

You must identify this document, read it, and keep it to hand. There will be a need to consult it throughout your dissertation study period.

Other formal rules may exist that will directly influence you, such as the requirement to attend a particular course of study as a co-requisite. For example, a statistics course. Are you required to submit an initial synopsis and / or make interim submissions or presentations on progress by particular dates? In all such cases these requirements must be met by the deadlines set. Will you be required to defend the work at a viva-voce or group discussion? If this is the case then you should start thinking in a 'defensive' manner now, that is, question yourself and your actions constantly. For example, can you justify why you stated this in the text or why you used that statistical method? (See also *The oral examination* chapter five).

Other rules can have an indirect impact. For example, your academic library may not process inter-library loans without your supervisor's signature on request forms; so remember to do this. Alternatively, the computer suite that houses your favourite statistical software is unavailable on Mondays; so make alternative arrangements, or use a different software package. Forgive me if I seem finicky or pedantic, but the fact is that rules <u>will</u> govern the way in which you approach your work and if you are not aware of them, or worse still choose to ignore them, then ultimately this will adversely affect your performance.

> TIP: Your dissertation stands a better chance of being successful if you identify and work to the rules governing it.

Regarding target readership. Typically, a dissertation will have one principal reader (i.e. your senior supervisor or Director of Studies) and several secondary readers (e.g. your second supervisor(s), external examiner(s), employer, other students[2]). You must however, write for your principal reader. After all, if s/he is satisfied with your work then the task is all but completed!

One way to consider this is by hypothetical example. Imagine your dissertation is investigating the role of computer-aided-design (CAD) in improving pre-contract efficiency. Further assume that you are a part time student working in an architect's office; an office that does not (yet!) agree with the merits of investment in CAD. If executed properly, your dissertation should underline the advantages of CAD technology and hence, how companies like that of your employer are somewhat 'blinkered' to innovation and progress. However, you obviously feel that to do this might not enhance your current employment prospects! Nevertheless, your supervisor (principal reader) will expect such a logical conclusion. So in this instance if you write to placate your secondary reader (employer), rather than your principal reader (supervisor), your grade may suffer.

Were the above a reality, one may reasonably advocate that you chose the wrong topic! However, albeit somewhat contrived, the scenario does underline the importance of writing for your principal reader.

---

[2]Most university libraries keep past dissertations either in hard copy or on microfilm for consultation by other students or researchers.

Planning the dissertation task

Every successful venture, from a touring holiday to a profitable corporate enterprise, will be based on a well thought out strategy represented by a realistic plan of action. A successful dissertation is no exception. A dissertation plan facilitates several things:

O   it confirms what should have been achieved at any particular point in time;

O   it confirms what you should be doing at any particular point in time; and

O   it forewarns of what has yet to be done.

Combined, the above offer a means of monitoring and hence controlling the task, so that (for example) should you start to fall behind then corrective action can be taken. Likewise, if you are completing activities far sooner than was programmed then either the plan is unrealistic; or the activities are not being adequately executed. In short, a plan encourages a proactive, instead of a reactive, approach to the task.

TIP: Compile a plan of work for your dissertation and monitor your progress. Take corrective action where necessary.

Essentially, a plan or strategy consists of two components: activities and respective timescales. Dissertation activities will be a function of many things including: the subject chosen, type of study being undertaken, research objectives and so on. Chapters two, three and four elucidate these activities, but for now we will observe how to formulate a plan using a simplified list of events -see Table 1.1.

We will assume that these activities (Column 1 of the Table) represent an undergraduate degree dissertation; to start at the beginning of an academic year in October and be completed by the following April. Also, for simplicity it is assumed at this planning stage that each calendar month consists of four weeks exactly; so the total timescale is 28 weeks.

Table 1.1. Simplified list of dissertation activities showing timescales and week numbers

Column 1: Activities considered	Column 2: Week No's allocated	Column 3: No. of weeks	Column 4: Cumulative time
Select topic	1 to 4	4	4
Literature search	5 to 8	4	8
Define objectives	9 to 10	2	10
Select methodology	11 to 12	2	12
Conduct research	13 to 16	4	16
Analyse data	17 to 18	2	18
Assimilate results	19 to 20	2	20
Draw conclusions	21 to 22	2	22
Write-up	23 to 26	4	26
Contingent	27 to 28	2	28

TOTAL TIME: 28 WEEKS

Although in reality each calendar month is longer than four weeks, such an approach helps 'build in' an extra contingent of time.

The next stage is to assign a set of realistic timescales to the activities and these are exhibited in columns two and three of Table 1.1. Column two identifies the respective week numbers against each of the activities (start date = week one) and finally, a cumulative timescale is shown in column four.

The advantages of developing a plan can now be clearly seen. For example, at exactly halfway through the dissertation period (week 14) we can establish that the objectives should have been clearly defined; that a suitable research methodology will have been selected; and that the student should be midway through the actual research component.

The inclusion of a contingent (weeks 27 and 28) is strongly advised. I have yet to supervise a student who did not feel that 'a few extra days' would have allowed final finishing touches to be applied to the work. Quite simply, I recommend that regardless of mode of study, you identify the official hand-in or completion date and instantly set your finishing deadline at least two weeks before this (the longer the research programme, the longer the contingent needs to be). You will be glad that you did!

Notwithstanding its usefulness, this initial plan is somewhat simplified and idealistic. For example, in reality the literature search will probably commence on week one when you begin looking for an appropriate topic (had you not decided already), and will continue almost throughout the entire programme. Likewise the dissertation write-up should begin very early on.

This is a very important point. I would not under any circumstances advocate that a dissertation be written at the end of the research. I strongly recommend you write constantly; as your work progresses. That way you will not forget things or have to make copious notes and, it is easier and more reliable to write about something whilst it is still fresh in your mind. Also, you cannot begin to edit your text until it is written, so starting early makes for a better narrative (see also chapter five). In my experience students feel more confident about their dissertation once they have got something down in writing. It seems the longer you defer starting; the harder it becomes to start.

> TIP: Begin writing your dissertation as soon as your topic is selected and your thinking on the subject has begun.

The write-up activity identified on the initial plan (weeks 23 to 26) should be primarily for final checking (chapter five). Furthermore, some activities will certainly overlap and not simply begin the day after the preceding one has finished. In view of this situation, it is well worth the effort to develop the initial plan one stage further and produce a bar (Gantt) chart that reflects more realistic conditions. The 'graphical' aspect of a bar chart is also much more meaningful in terms of understanding what should have been completed and / or should be in progress at any given time. Such a chart is neither difficult nor time consuming to produce, indeed, most built environment students should have been familiarised with them as part of their (planning) studies.

Incidentally, if you are competent with one of the many computer planning programmes available then it is well worth using it, they are particularly useful for determining the *critical path* and will therefore easily highlight potential time or activity overlap problems.

Figure 1.2. shows a bar chart, developed from the activities and timescales discussed in the initial plan formulated above.

Dissertation structure: the 'three component' concept

The three component concept sub-divides any communication task into three distinct components. For example, in the case of public speaking then a suitable structure would be:

O   tell the audience what you are going to say;
O   say it;
O   tell the audience what you've said!

These components can more seriously be described as: (i) the introduction to the speech; (ii) the main body of the speech; and (iii) a summary of the salient points conveyed to the audience. So what does public speaking have to do with a dissertation? Well, in many ways the two are very much the same. To understand this we may firstly transform the above verbal structure into the structure of a logically presented, formal, written report as follows:

O   the beginning i.e. introductory text;
O   the middle i.e. main body of the report; and
O   the end e.g. conclusions.

Figure 1.2.
Bar chart showing overlap of activities

Activity	Week number: 1	2	3	4	5	6	7	8	9	10	11	12	13	14	15	16	17	18	19	20	21	22	23	24	25	26	27	28
Select topic																												
Literature search																												
Define objectives																												
Select methodology																												
Conduct research																												
Analyse data																												
Assimilate results																												
Draw conclusions																												
Write up																												
Contingent																												

Key: = as per outline plan

= timescale allowing for overlap of activities

In a typical dissertation (which is after all a kind of report), these components will overlap slightly but nonetheless they will be there. By forming the necessary 'links' between them we may describe a complete dissertation as follows:

Component one is the beginning. This is described as the introduction and will consist of; introductory text (e.g. review of the literature); and a statement of objectives and / or working hypothesis.

> *The first component of a dissertation may be linked to the second component by indicating how the objectives might be met and the basis of that decision.*

Component two is the middle. This is described as the main body of the dissertation and will consist of; an explanation of the research methodology; a description of research undertaken; and analysis of research data.

> *The second component of a dissertation may be linked to the third by stating salient findings of the research (analysis) and how these compare with the literature.*

Component three is the end. This is described as the conclusion and will consist of; interpretation of the research findings; abstraction of conclusions; and possibly recommendations.

> *The end of a dissertation may ultimately be linked to the beginning by comparison of what the research discovered and what was expected. That is, was the dissertation objective achieved? or hypothesis proven / disproved?*

This final link (end to beginning) is important: a dissertation should be thought of as being 'circular in nature' i.e. to end at the original starting point. This may at first seem illogical, but Figure 1.3. clarifies the concept.

Figure 1.3. The circular nature of a dissertation

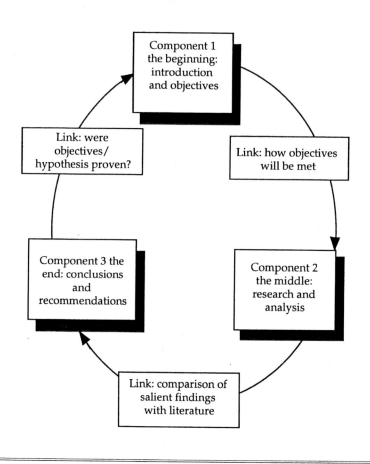

Good writing avoids leaving gaps; these open up voids in the subconscious mind of a reader. Voids lead to a loss of concentration and what is perceived as a 'fragmented' text. There must be logical direction from one component (or theme) of writing to the next. That way the reader does not get lost or bored, and the text (hopefully!) makes sense.

I like to think of this aspect of writing as follows: imagine leading a blindfolded person by the hand, through a room full of obstacles. If you let go of their hand it is only a matter of time before that person would get lost. If you fail to adequately guide your reader then they will lose their way also.

Having identified the three component concept, we may now concentrate a little more on the structure of a dissertation, particularly, the structure of each component itself. However, it must be appreciated that no one single structure will accommodate all possible situations. Changes will have to take account of the topic, research methods used, statistical or other analyses to be described and so on.

A model dissertation structure now follows which when considered jointly with the detailed treatment of each component later (chapters two, three and four), will allow a modified version to be devised for any given research scenario. The model is based on the three component concept described above.

> TIP: Try and establish your dissertation structure early on. Even if this structure is prone to changes it will still give your work some direction.

Component one: The beginning

- preliminary material: title page; abstract; copyright page; acknowledgements; preface; list of contents; list of tables; list of figures; list of appendices
- first chapter: general introduction
- early chapter: literature review
- early chapter: emphasis of specific subject / aspect to be investigated
- early chapter: confirmation of objectives / hypothesis
- link with second component.

Component two: The middle

- main chapter: research methodology used
- main chapter: other research information such as limitations, investigation parameters, experimentation design, the sample composition, etc.
- main chapter: data collection and analysis
- main chapter: abstraction of salient findings
- main chapter: presentation of salient findings (may be included with last)
- link with third component.

Component three: The end

- end chapter: discussion of the findings
- end chapter: abstraction of firm conclusions
- final chapter: derivation of logical recommendations and concluding link with beginning (may be included with last)
- references / bibliography / references and bibliography combined / further reading
- appendices.

It must be reinforced that the above model is dynamic and prone to variation. Certain chapters may be omitted whilst others may have to be incorporated to accurately reflect the work undertaken. Alternatively, several chapters may be merged into one.

Summary of the fundamentals

❑ Two main types of research are applied and pure. Applied research attempts to improve or resolve practical problems whilst pure research tends to address more theoretical issues.

❑ Applied (built environment) research tends to address problems by modelling them and observing the effects of applying changes to them.

❏ Pure research is generally a feature of undergraduate and postgraduate dissertations. Applied research is more likely to be a characteristic of higher degrees such as the PhD.

❏ A dissertation may be classified as being either a first degree (e.g. Hons); postgraduate (e.g. MSc); or higher degree by research (e.g. MPhil). A thesis generally represents a contribution to knowledge (e.g. PhD).

❏ Selection of dissertation topic will involve consideration of several factors including: student ability; student area of interest; availability of information; timescale; the supervisor; amount of research required; type of research required; degree of objectivity required; and needs of current / future employer.

❏ The rules governing dissertation study will vary according to circumstance. In successful dissertations they are identified and adhered to.

❏ The overall dissertation task must be planned by careful consideration of necessary activities and respective timescales. The final plan is best represented in the form of a bar (Gantt) chart for easy assimilation and monitoring of progress.

❏ A good dissertation will essentially consist of (and be undertaken in) three distinct components: the beginning; the middle; and the end. The beginning introduces the work, the middle will present the research and the end will conclude matters.

❏ Dissertation structure will be a function of: topic; methods employed; analysis used, etc. In short, the structure will need to reflect the needs of each individual dissertation setting.

❏ The dissertation experience should be enjoyed!

Chapter two
First component: The beginning

This chapter explains the following points:

- ❏ how a dissertation should be formatted
- ❏ what the preliminary pages of a dissertation should contain
- ❏ how to write the introductory text and literature review
- ❏ how to cite references within the text
- ❏ the importance of confirming dissertation objectives

Out of intense complexities intense simplicities emerge
(W. Churchill 1874-1965)

Introduction

This chapter offers advice with respect to the first distinct component of a dissertation: *The beginning*. It deals with writing your introductory text. The beginning is important, if you get it right, then your reader's journey through the remainder of the dissertation will be mapped out. If you get the beginning wrong, then their journey may be a difficult one.

Dissertation format

Having looked at the overall structure of a dissertation in the previous chapter, we will now observe in much more detail each aspect of the first component: *The beginning*. First, you must determine how the dissertation needs to be presented, i.e. *formatted*. In terms of format, the following will be considered:

- O   page size
- O   font size and type
- O   spacing
- O   margins
- O   headers and footers
- O   titles and headings
- O   miscellaneous conventions
- O   cover sheets and binding.

Before discussing these, the student is reminded that ultimately, format must be in accordance with the relevant academic regulations governing the dissertation (refer *Identifying the rules*, chapter one).

Page size

This is typically A4 in the UK. A page size larger than A4 means that the production of microfiche copies and / or full size reproduction of the dissertation, may not be feasible. (Some academic institutions and the British Library Document Supply centre, store and reproduce for research purposes, dissertations in this way). Typeface should be on one side of the page only, unless regulations stipulate otherwise. A good quality plain cartridge paper is essential, sufficiently opaque to avoid show-through of the print (minimum $80g / M^2$ is recommended). Embossed papers do not really add to presentation; they merely falsely pad out the dissertation, detail can sometimes be difficult to read because of the embossment or grain and they can 'jam' in certain types of printer.

Font size and type

The text should be compiled on a word processor. To consider otherwise is ineffective, particularly, in terms of ability to edit early drafts of the text. If you are working on a computer, start with two brand new disks and keep these solely for your dissertation, nothing else. Make one disk the 'master' and the other a 'back-up' disk. Create a new file (this may otherwise be called a document, depending on the computer system being used) for each new chapter of the dissertation on the master disk. Work only on this master disk. As your write-up of the dissertation progresses, be certain to regularly make copies of the master disk onto the backup disk. Be careful to store the master and back-up disks in different places, so that should one become damaged or lost, then the amount of work to be re-typed is kept to a minimum.

TIP: Always back-up your work and keep the master and back-up disks in safe, different places.

Modern word processors offer a tremendous range of fonts (styles of typeface). However, I recommend that you use either one of the following:

This is plain Times font, **this is bold Times font** *and this is italic Times font.*

This is plain Courier font, **this is bold Courier font** *and this is italic Courier font.*

This is plain Bookman font, **this is bold Bookman font** *and this is italic Bookman font.*

This is plain Helvetica font, **this is bold Helvetica font** *and this is italic Helvetica font.*

The first two fonts are compatible with most printers (Sprent, 1995). Obviously, you must select a font that your chosen printer is able to deal with. If you wish to contrast a particular piece of text with the main text, then use a contrasting typeface. That is, if the main text is in (say) Times, then contrast with something like Helvetica. These two choices contrast well because the former is *serif* whilst the latter is *sans serif*. *Serifs* are the embellishments at the extremities of characters: these are better appreciated if large text is examined:

TIMES (serif)   Helvetica (sans serif)

Most word processors also have a range of options regarding font style. However, you must resist temptation: do not overdo the **bold**, *italic*, underline, double underline, outline, shadow etc. You can appreciate by looking at the last sentence, that to mix styles in this way causes an untidy and confusing text. It is much better to save these goodies for highlighting such things as Latin words (italic), important statements (may be bold, italic or underline), titles (see later) and so on.

Size of font is also very important. The large text used above for comparison of Times and Helvetica (serif and sans serif) is much too big for the main body of text. Twelve point font (12 pt.) is easy and comfortable to read and is a sensible size for dissertations. Finally:

- O   **avoid using bold for the main text**
- O   *avoid using italics for the main text*
- O   DO NOT USE CAPITALS FOR THE MAIN TEXT
- O   *do not use fancy fonts other than on wedding invitations!*

Further guidance regarding fonts, typefaces and size of text may be observed in a BRE occasional paper called *Write it right* (Brewer, 1994).

Spacing

The spacing between lines of text is as important as font type and size. Double spacing is normal for the main body of text. This is also a good habit to get into when word processing early drafts of any text, because it provides space between the lines for editing (see chapter five). Likewise, it also provides space for your supervisor to write feedback to you as s/he she reads your early draft chapters.

Double spaced text is also a lot easier to read (compared to single spaced). To understand this better, take two pages of text: one small font, single spaced; the other a larger font, double spaced. Regardless of subject matter, just a cursory glance at these samples will confirm that the larger, double spaced text is easier to read. Imagine how your principal reader will feel if presented with a dissertation typed in single spaced, small text! An exception can be Tables or Figures containing many rows of numerals, these may be single, or one-and-a-half line spaced (see chapter three).

It is normal to insert an extra space (empty line) between paragraphs (e.g. as between this sentence and the last) and at least one or even two extra spaces, between the end of a paragraph and a new title or sub-title. There is also a school of preference for a space below each title and the first (following) sentence. Personally, I do not see the need for this in a dissertation, because of the fact that the text is double spaced anyway.

Regarding *chapter* titles, always begin a new chapter on a new page. Personally, I advise against inserting chapter heading pages (i.e. a page with nothing more than the chapter title on it). These serve no purpose whatsoever other than to pad out a weak dissertation! Finally, do not leave blank spaces within the text unless: i) they follow the end of a chapter; or ii) they are above or below a Table or Figure (and to enter text into that space would mean 'cramming' too much onto one page).

Margins

These should be ample: too big is better than too small. Twenty five millimetres (one inch) is a 'rule of thumb' for top, bottom and right hand margins. A larger margin of at least 37 millimetres (one-and-a-half inches) is more suitable for the left hand side of the page to allow for binding. Where text must be on both sides of the paper remember that the wider margin will be on alternate sides of the pages. So use 37 millimetre margins on both vertical sides, unless the word processing software allows for this automatically. If numbers are being used for titles (see below) then make allowance for these in the left hand margin or, line the numbers up with the main text. These two options are exhibited in Figure 2.1.

Figure 2.1. Left hand margins

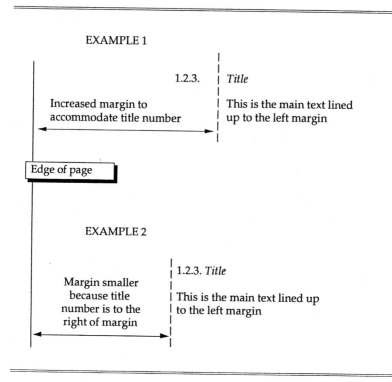

Headers and footers

Most word processing software packages provide a header and footer facility. This allows information to be inserted at the top or bottom of a page respectively; so that this information will then be automatically carried onto each new page of the computer file (or document) thereafter. A typical dissertation header will exhibit the chapter number tight to the left hand margin and the chapter title, tight to the right hand margin like so:

Chapter 6   Laboratory experiments undertaken

Note that the size of font in a header is normally smaller than the main text; so that it does not detract the reader from the main text. Typically, set headers and footers two points smaller e.g. main text twelve point, header 10 point.

The footer normally contains the page number tight to the right hand margin (unless regulations ask for it to be centred). Most word processing software has a 'starting page number' facility so that if chapter one ends on page 20, then chapter two can be programmed to start on page 21 (it is imperative that pages are numbered consecutively throughout the entire dissertation). This facility is essential if the chapters are stored on different computer files (documents). I personally dislike the 'page 35 of 87' facility because it appears too clumsy. The left hand side of a footer may contain peripheral information if required like so:

F. Smith. Dissertation   89

Be careful not to include too much information in the footer and header or you will clutter up the page. Finally, if you have selected a font style for the main text that is not the default setting (i.e. not the font that the computer sets automatically), be sure to use your same chosen font style in the header and footer also. It is wrong to mix two different fonts in one document unless for contrasting purposes as described earlier.

Titles and headings

Here is something that calls for consistency: select a suitable hierarchy for titles at an early stage and <u>adhere to it</u> throughout the work. For example:

CHAPTER TITLES GIVEN IN BOLD 14 POINT CAPITALS

Main headings given in bold 12 point text
Sub-headings given in plain 12 point text
sub, sub-headings given in italic 12 point text.

The above is a suggested hierarchy only and by no means the optimal solution. Try not to sub divide the text further than sub, sub-headings (other than with paragraphs themselves). To do so causes confusion. Further, in the above hierarchy of titles it was assumed that the main text was 12 point and hence, everything except the chapter title is 12 point also.

It is convenient here to discuss the numbering of sections; the use of such numbers in a dissertation being optional (Preece, 1994). This formal approach may be disliked by some, but I advocate it, because it assists in emphasising the paragraph arrangement and facilitates precise cross-referencing. The numbering must of course coincide with the list of contents (see later). The following format may be used:

1.0.   **Main heading 0 of chapter 1**
 1.0.1.   Sub-heading 1, of main heading 0, of chapter 1
 1.0.2.   Sub-heading 2, of main heading 0, of chapter 1
  1.0.2.1.   *Sub, sub-heading 1 of sub-heading 2,*
  of main heading 0, of chapter 1.

Note also that my suggested hierarchy of title styles has been applied.

Figures and Tables within chapter one will be in numeric order preceded by 1 (i.e. for chapter one) e.g. Figures 1.1, 1.2, 1.3 etc. and Tables 1.1, 1.2, 1.3, 1.4 etc. Likewise, for chapter six we then could have:

6.3.   **Main heading 3 of chapter 6**
 6.3.1.   Sub-heading 1, of main heading 3, of chapter 6
  6.3.1.1.   *Sub, sub-heading 1, of sub-heading*
  1, of main heading 3, of chapter 6.

Chapter six Figures will be numbered 6.1, 6.2, 6.3 etc. and Tables numbered 6.1, 6.2, 6.3, 6.4 etc. Do not subdivide headings further than shown for the reasons given earlier regarding clarity. It is worthwhile dedicating some time to logically assigning headings to the work, because these will serve to guide the reader through the dissertation. No headings at all, too few headings, or too many headings and the dissertation will be confusing and difficult to follow.

TIP: You can develop a provisional dissertation structure, select a suitable hierarchy of titles and number all headings in one exercise. That way, you will develop a logical framework around which to write the main text. A typical framework is shown in Appendix A. If you choose to do this, refer to the previous sections (titles, headings and numbering) and, the section on overall dissertation structure, given at the end of chapter one.

Miscellaneous format conventions

Numbers are expressed in Arabic numerals. One school of thought is that it is acceptable to express the numbers one to ten in numerals i.e. 1, 2, 3, . . .10 and above 10, the number should be typewritten e.g. eleven, twelve, thirteen (Manheimer, 1973). The opposite school of thought is to use numerals to express numbers 10 and above, and words to express numbers below 10 (Rudestam and Newton, 1992 p187). In my opinion the latter option is tidier, but the context of the narrative will have major influence on choice. For example, a statistical discussion using many numbers is best expressed in numerals for the sake of readability, like this:

"Minimum was 0.01, maximum 0.99, this giving a range of 0.98. The mean was 0.50, the median 0.52. Standard error was 0.04 and standard deviation 0.30. Fifty observations were considered".

Notice that where a new sentence begins with a number (i.e. Fifty) then that number is typewritten; do not start a new sentence with Arabic numerals. Whilst on the subject of statistics, percentages should be written out within the text as two words e.g. 62 per cent, 90 per cent, but expressed using the percentage sign in Tables e.g. 62%, 90%. Decimals should always be expressed as numerals e.g. 6.2 per cent, 9.0 per cent, and columns of decimals should be lined up vertically in Tables (etc.) using the decimal point.

Footnotes (see number[1] below) should be avoided where possible. These tend to distract the reader from the main text and make pages look a little untidy. Try and incorporate the (footnote) information into a follow-on sentence or alternatively, use parentheses (brackets like these). However, be careful that the follow-on sentences do not make the text unwieldy, and be careful not to overuse brackets because these can cause 'fragmentation' of the text. In short, use footnotes only when you want to include additional information which, if included in the text would 'clutter' the original statement being made.

Abbreviations are acceptable but do not be presumptuous. Present the abbreviation in full the first time you use it within the text and put the abbreviated letters in brackets directly afterwards e.g. "This information was obtained from The Chartered Institute of Building (CIOB)". Then, the next time CIOB appears in the text a reader will know what it means. Do not overuse abbreviations to the point that the text completely looses its meaning. The same principles apply to technical jargon and specialist phrases. Wherever possible do not assume the reader knows what they mean (to try and be 'clever' only causes irritation). In short, avoid technical jargon if you can. Remember: good writing is clear and easy to understand.

Cover sheets and binding

Before binding, print out a good quality copy of your dissertation preferably by laser printer. If several bound copies are required, then

---

[1] This numeral corresponds with that in the above text: this is footnote number one.

obtain the necessary number of photocopies but be sure that: i) the photocopies are of good quality; ii) they do not contain any blank or damaged pages; and iii) all pages are in correct sequence. If an external examiner has to check or grade the work, it is worthwhile finding out whether or not a temporary bound copy (e.g. plastic comb or Lever arch file) will suffice. That way, any corrections required by the examiner can be performed prior to final print out, and subsequent final binding or covering.

There are three principal options for binding. The first is to face the document with a clear plastic cover sheet through which the title page can be seen in full. In this instance the dissertation is normally bound using a 'plastic comb' on the spine. Plastic combs are practical: they allow the document to be opened and lay flat easily without damage. They also facilitate subsequent photocopying (where this is allowed). Avoid heat glue binders if possible, they are difficult to set in place properly and tend to restrict the opening / turning of pages. Be sure to include all relevant details on the title page (see specimen exhibited in Appendix B) and be sure that it is a top quality, preferably laser, print out. The use of colour may also be considered for the title page. Albeit we should not 'judge a book by its cover' this effort is worthwhile, good presentation goes a long way towards satisfying a reader (your supervisor!). Also, be sure that the clear plastic cover is not scratched or marked.

The second option is to use a standard cover board or sheet, as defined (or supplied) by the academic institution. These are also normally used in conjunction with plastic comb binders, so many of the previous comments apply. Where an aperture is provided in the cover board, be careful to correctly align the necessary information (title etc.) on the title sheet, so that it shows through the aperture unimpeded.

The third option is to have the work professionally bound. This is normally the requirement for higher research degree dissertations. Again, consult the relevant academic guide for allowable colours (some institutions define the colouring of binding and lettering) and, for confirmation of required lettering size and format to the face sheet and spine. Most academic institution libraries have a list of suitable binding companies along with current price lists.

In order to achieve consistency throughout your dissertation you can adopt this procedure: Set up your first computer file (document) containing settings and choices for font type and size, margin sizes, headers, footers, spelling options etc. Name this file 'chapter one'. Copy, or duplicate this file onto your workdisk several times, naming each new copy 'chapter two, chapter three' etc. Obviously, each new chapter (file) will require some adjustment in terms of starting page number, header content, footer content and so on. However, using this procedure ensures that each chapter will have similar default settings and hence, they will all be consistent.

TIP: If you format your chapters as a template i.e. margins, headers, font, spacing etc. then consistency will be achieved throughout the dissertation.

In summary, adhere to the academic regulations regarding format and aim for simple logic, tidiness and clarity.

Dissertation content: the preliminary pages

We will now consider the preliminary pages of a dissertation. Previous comments regarding the governing regulations and variation of contents to suit the given setting apply here also. Preliminaries now discussed are:

- O   title page
- O   abstract
- O   copyright page
- O   declaration
- O   acknowledgements

O   dedication
O   preface
O   lists of: contents, figures, tables and appendices.

The above are normally presented within a dissertation in this same order.

Title page

This is located directly beneath the clear cover sheet, cover board, or inside front cover of bound dissertations. It should include the title; author name; author qualifications; to which academic institution and for which degree the work is submitted; and the date (month / year). In some cases it is required to include the supervisor(s) name also. Unless a cover board with an aperture is being used, all text should be double spaced and sensibly positioned as to take up the majority of the page. Aim for an almost symmetrical layout that neither looks top or bottom heavy. See the example title page given in Appendix B.

Abstract

An abstract should summarise the entire contents of a dissertation. It needs to be very carefully thought out and written to accurately perform this function. The abstract is sometimes referred to as a summary, but this is not strictly correct because a summary normally only contains conclusions and recommendations.

Consider an abstract as follows: If a 'stranger' was to read your dissertation abstract could they subsequently tell you; what broad subject area was studied, what specific objective or hypothesis was investigated, how this was done and what the salient findings and recommendations of the dissertation were? If so, then the abstract is satisfactory. If not, the abstract has not been adequately written and will require more detailed attention!

Also, consider that in the case of UK higher degrees the abstract will possibly be read by many people; predominantly other researchers. This is because it will be reproduced in the *Index to British Theses* (ASLIB, 1994). By all means draft out the abstract early on, but re-write or edit it when the dissertation is finished, since you will run the risk of it reflecting what the dissertation was *supposed* to have contained! Regarding length, it should take up no more than one side of A4 (about 200-300 words).

Copyright page

This is where academic regulations must be consulted. Normally, the author shall own, and continue to own, the copyright. However, by virtue of submitting the work for assessment this usually grants the examining academic institution a royalty free licence to do several things. These may include: to copy from the dissertation; to issue or show the work; to broadcast the work; to publish or make adaptations from the work and so on. To identify that copyright rests with the author, the following convention is used: "© Copyright 1996 F.J. Yourname." The word 'Copyright' is optional. Further, the above need not necessarily be on a page of its own, it could for example be at the foot of the title page.

Declaration

Some academic regulations require the student to insert a declaration page that confirms originality of the work. (An alternative to this is that the student signs a separate declaration form upon submission of the dissertation). Typically, a declaration page will exhibit a statement to the effect:

Declaration
The author hereby confirms that this work or any part thereof (or. . . this work in part or in full. . .) has not been previously submitted to this or any other body in respect of any other award or for any other purposes.

Alternatively, where previously submitted work does form part of the dissertation then a paragraph to the following effect will be included:

The author hereby acknowledges that the work listed below has previously been submitted for assessment elsewhere:
  i. (item [i] explained here) page 12
  ii. (item [ii] explained here) pages 67 to 69 inclusive.
The supervisor of this work has authorised that such inclusion in this dissertation is appropriate.

This would typically be the case when (for example) aspects of a subject investigated at first degree level, are used as the basis for further research at higher degree level.

Acknowledgements

These are essentially a thank you, to all who contributed directly or otherwise to the study. They should be expressed as simply as possible and may include any of the following: supervisor(s); Director of research; collaborating institutions; collaborating industrial partners; sources of financial grant or support; and so forth.

Dedication

A student may wish to dedicate the work to something, or someone. This is a matter of personal choice and very often includes family.

Preface

A preface or foreword is only really necessary where early explanation of the work (that could not logically be fitted into the general introduction) is required. This might be the case for particularly specific, or scientifically oriented research. A preface may also include acknowledgements.

List(s) of contents

Following the above preliminaries, a list of contents is usually given and this will show all that is included in the dissertation. See Figure 2.2.

Figure 2.2. Sample list of contents

List of contents	*Page*
Preface............	ii
List of chapters........	iii
List of tables.........	iv
List of figures........	v
List of appendices.......	viii
Chapters............	1 to 97
References...........	98 to 108
Appendices..........	109 to 114

Note that pages prior to the main chapters (i.e. preliminaries discussed above) are numbered using Roman numerals. Arabic numerals are used for page numbers commencing with the first page of chapter one.

The list of contents is followed on a new page by the list of chapters. Having already discussed titles and numbering of headings, this is quite simply a matter of using the same format but with page numbers also shown; see Figure 2.3. The lists of tables, figures and appendices appear next and are relatively straightforward; see Figure 2.4.

These four lists (chapters, tables, figures, appendices) will each commence on a new page, and the text is best double spaced for clarity and consistency.

Figure 2.3. Sample list of chapters

List of chapters *Page*

Figure 2.4. Sample list of tables, figures and appendices

List of Tables *Page*

List of Figures

List of Appendices

Dissertation content: the introductory chapters and literature review

The introductory chapters within this first component (the beginning) of a dissertation will normally include: a 'general' introduction; the literature review; an explanation of the specific aspect to be investigated; and identification of the dissertation objectives / hypothesis.

We will now look at the first two of these, that is, the general introduction and literature review. Following this, the correct approach to referencing will be explained. Although referencing is intrinsically linked to the literature review, I have dealt with it separately because it is worthy of detailed discussion. The identification of objectives or hypothesis is explained in the penultimate section of this chapter.

The general introduction

Regardless of topic or nature of the investigation, every dissertation (or any other formal written work for that matter) should commence with a general introduction. In this context the word general means a relatively broad discussion, that is, a logical lead-in to the subject. However, this does not mean that the introduction will be simplistic; it should in fact be quite detailed.

Perhaps the easiest way to understand the function of an introduction, is to think of it in terms of a practical analogy. Imagine you are to show somebody around your home for the very first time. First, you will enter through the front door and warmly invite your visitor inside. The dissertation introduction also starts in such a logical fashion: at the very beginning (you did not enter your house halfway up the stairs through a landing window!). Also, the text needs to be like that invitation extended to your visitor: a gentle, warm "step this way".

In terms of the guided tour, you will go on to show your visitor around: the lounge; the kitchen; the bedrooms; the bathroom and so on. Likewise, your introduction should now start to 'show the reader around' the subject area: some background; other topics that are related to this one; why you chose the topic (or house - get the idea?) etc. Whilst touring the home, you will probably mention intended improvements such as; "this room is going to be decorated" and that; "we wish to build an extension there". In terms of your dissertation introduction, you should also indicate the intended structure and route that the work will take; "this will be looked at" and why and; "that topic will be considered because" etc. It may seem strange to consider the introduction in this way but the 'showing someone around' analogy perfectly represents what the dissertation introduction is intended to do.

TIP: Use the introduction to 'invite your reader in' and explain the intended route of your dissertation.

After dealing with the broad, more general aspects of the topic in the introduction, the text should subsequently tell the reader what specific angle(s) will be concentrated upon. Obviously, this will primarily be a function of the literature surrounding the topic. That is, perhaps an area was identified in the literature for which little previous research has been performed and that therefore, this is the avenue your work will pursue. This 'more specific' component should be well referenced, citing a broad range of literature that helped formulate (your thinking and hence) its structure. Let us now consider the literature search and critical review in some detail.

The literature review

It has been suggested that generally, students do not fully understand the purpose of investigating the literature related to their chosen topic (Leedy, 1989). Personal experience leads me to agree with this contention. To properly execute and derive the best from a literature review, a student needs to understand what it is, and why it is performed.

What is it? A literature review is the compilation and assimilation of as much information as can be discovered with respect to a given topic.

Why is it performed? In this context the review enables a student to fully understand the current status of a topic, to subsequently consolidate thinking about the topic, and identify the best way forward to advance that chosen area of research. The review will help you to:

○ understand the peripheral issues
○ reveal the extent to which research and current understanding has reached
○ identify the key variables impacting upon the topic
○ suggest routes to take with regard to advancing knowledge or understanding of the topic
○ suggest routes with regard to solving issues surrounding the topic
○ yield sources of data
○ help generate other ideas
○ compare your ideas and thinking with respect to existing knowledge.

We will now investigate the literature review in more detail, under the headings of: the information search; the assimilation of information; and the review write-up.

The literature review and information search

A successful review is reliant upon thorough and detailed discovery of all relevant literature. Once under way, the search does in fact become easier, that is, upon discovery of some well referenced, relevant material. For example, just one (say) PhD thesis that deals with an aspect of the chosen topic will yield many, many references. In turn, some of these references will themselves yield further items of relevance. This aspect of 'getting the ball rolling' is shown graphically in Figure 2.5. There are a multitude of literature sources many of which are now discussed. Since previous dissertations are one of the better sources, we will discuss these first.

The *Index to Theses with abstracts accepted for higher degrees of Great Britain, Ireland and The Council for National Academic Awards* (ASLIB, 1994), contains abstracts of all dissertations submitted for higher degrees, as qualified by the Index title. The Index is produced annually and is an excellent starting point for any determined literature search. At the rear of each volume is an alphabetical keyword index. Let us assume that your chosen topic wanted to investigate the future potential of bridge construction using modern lightweight materials. Then the Index could be scanned for relevant keywords which in this instance might include: bridges, materials, plastics, glass reinforced plastic and glass reinforced concrete, as a starting point.

Against each keyword listed[2] will be all dissertations submitted that year[3] which have these keywords in their title. Subsequently, you may turn to the respective pages of the volume and read each abstract to determine whether or not, that particular dissertation will be of interest to you. Should this be the case then a full copy of the dissertation may be ordered via your academic library. Dissertations requested in this way are most often supplied from the British Library Document Supply Centre (BLDSC); normally on microfilm, but sometimes in hard copy.

The researcher's most useful source of literature is the library. There are two sources of library material: public libraries and the academic institution library. Public libraries should not be discounted but most of what they contain is 'general' in nature and hence of limited use. However, two particular areas in which the public library can sometimes excel is the reference section and local archive information. It is obviously impossible to generalise with respect to what a given library will contain, but suffice to say that the reference section is well worth a visit. Regarding archives, 'central' public libraries often keep a comprehensive collection of local, archival material that can be invaluable to those topics centred on a local theme. For example, should a chronology of local ordnance survey maps be required.

---

[2] It may be that not all are listed, so other keywords may need to be established.

[3] Obviously it makes sense to start with the current year and work backwards.

Figure 2.5. Graphical overview of the literature search

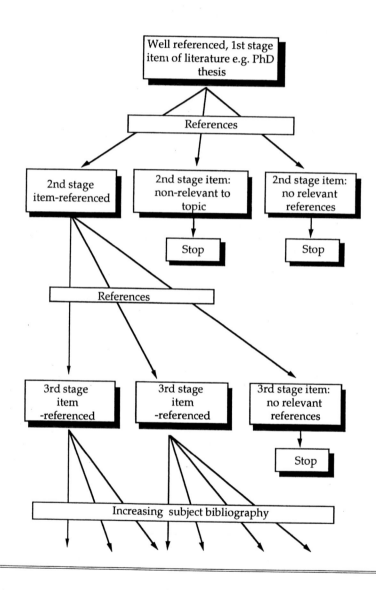

The academic institution library is beyond doubt the best all-round source of information. You are advised to become acquainted with your subject librarian at an early stage! You will get more from your library the more that you learn how to use it. However, here lies a skill that will have to be learned the hard way: each hour spent searching the shelves is time well spent. This is indeed one task that becomes easier with experience.

Learn how to find your way around: identify which areas contain what and what shelf-marks are applicable to your particular areas of interest, etc. (A shelf-mark is the subject number on the spine of a book that libraries use to assign material to a particular class, and hence, particular geographical location within the library).

Learn how to use the library computer system. This will normally facilitate author; author and title; title alone; and keyword searches. Author search finds all items held by a particular author or items about as well as by, individuals or organisations. Author and title search is useful if the author (or editor) and title of a particular item is known. Title search will find the location of an item if the exact title is known. Keyword search is the most useful feature for research. It finds all library material (based on the keywords entered) and brings these together in one list. Hence, to refer to the bridge scenario discussed earlier, then the chosen keywords may be inserted into the computer and it be instructed to search for all material that the library holds showing correlation between each keyword(s) and literature title(s). Other features of the library computer facility normally include: library stock (books, periodicals, videos, microfilm, etc.); status of material (on loan / in stock / short loan / reference only); automatic reservations; automatic renewals; and location of items.

Academic libraries also tend to stock (normally the better) examples of dissertations from former students. Again, here it is worthwhile scanning the shelves to see what is available. Even if nothing very closely related to your chosen topic can be found, some dissertations may deal with related issues and hence provide the possibility of helpful references within their bibliographic listings.

TIP: Become familiar with your academic library as soon as possible in your dissertation studies. Learn to utilise fully, all of the resources offered.

CD-Roms are another priceless source of information normally offered as an academic library facility. CD-ROM databases contain vast amounts of information on specific subjects and in view that this is a 'modern' technology, the range of databases is increasing at an alarming rate. Four examples are: British Standards; INSPEC; The Guardian; and Tech-Index (this list by no means exhaustive!).

The British Standards database is normally updated every 30 days and is accessed initially by using an index disk (unless the computer is networked to a server). Searches for information may be made via: a known standard number e.g. BS. 5930 (Site investigations); by keyword, where word(s) are entered describing or allied to the topic; or by organisation - which restricts the search to a set of known organisations. The relevant British Standard may then be inspected on the computer screen or printed out in part or in full (if printing facilities are available). It must be mentioned at this point that Copyright restrictions should be identified where applicable and strictly adhered to. The librarian will be able to assist in this direction.

INSPEC offers references and abstracts compiled from over 4 300 technical journals and reports, covering the subjects of physics, electronics, computing and information technology. Keyword, thesaurus and index searches are available.

The Guardian offers a search of back copies by way of date or section of newspaper, to search headlines only, or articles from a certain place or by a certain correspondent.

Tech-Index is a subset of Compendex; an engineering / technology database and it includes coverage of building and construction. Searches are initiated in a similar manner to those described above.

Other CD-ROM data bases include: ERIC (education related material); ABI INFORM (business information); PsychLIT (psychology and related disciplines); SOCIOFILE (sociology and related disciplines); and Social Sciences Index (see Rudestam and Newton, 1992 p172). In short, CD-ROM is a very efficient method of searching for data or literature. Liaise with your institutional library, and fully capitalise on any CD-ROM facilities offered.

Another modern information source is the ever growing INTERNET: the information super-highway. Amongst other things, the NET (as it is affectionately known) offers keyword searches, initiated in a similar way to those already described. Information uncovered may be viewed on screen or in hard copy if printed. The process is too comprehensive to fully describe in this book and the volume of information accessible even greater to try and comprehend! Identify how you can access the NET and learn by using it, the time taken is well worthwhile. Also, take note that most construction journals have their own Internet pages and can offer a keyword search of all back-issues.

Here are the locations of some very useful building / construction research oriented NET information sources:

O   Construction Management and Economics journal (published by E and FN Spon) database offering search facilities:
http://www.bre.polyu.edu.hk/search/jocme.html

O   American Society of Civil Engineers, civil engineering database:
http://www.pubs.asce.org/cedbsrch.html

O   Crisp (The Construction Research and Innovation Strategy Panel) provides a search of several thousand research projects:
http://www.crisp.rdg.ac.uk

O   The University of Wolverhampton internet resources in Engineering and Construction:
http://www.wlv.ac.uk/lib/systems/sebegate.htm.

Another feature of the NET is electronic mail (E-mail). This allows instant communication with fellow researchers / students / industrial contacts, the world over. Also, there are several dedicated built environment E-mail research networks, that anyone conducting research can join at no cost. These provide opportunity to request help, exchange ideas or debate research issues. However, please do not abuse these facilities by placing requests for information that could be found elsewhere relatively easily. All involved in research are expected to do some legwork! Learn how to utilise E-mail fully.

Barbour Index offers information specific to construction. This is another index available on CD-ROM, but the microfiche system is now described because CD-ROM access is virtually the same as that described earlier. A series of hardback Indexes list all subjects contained on the fiches *viz*; Technical; Facilities Management; Building Products; Health and Safety; Project Management.

The Building Products microfile for example, contains information on design; construction; building science; legislation; standards; codes of practice; reports from UK and EC parliaments; government departments; professional bodies; research institutions; trade associations and publishers (Barbour, 1996).

Once a subject has been found in the relevant 'index to subjects' the subjects section of the book may then be observed where information is arranged by publisher. A fiche number and frame reference is then given, (i.e. the relevant fiche and specific frame upon it) and that particular frame may then be observed on the microfiche screen. Again, printing facilities may be available but Copyright restrictions must be observed. Update packs for Barbour Index are available every four months thereby keeping the system up to date.

In a similar vein to Barbour, the RIBA*ti* Technical Information Microfile provides a collection of technical information (RIBA, 1996). The main index contains full texts of: British Standards and Codes of Practice cited in the Building Regulations for England and Wales and the Building Standards for Scotland; British Standards and Codes of Practice cited in the National Building Specification; publications from the American

Society of Testing and Materials and Factory Mutual International; a selection of legislation; Building Research Establishment Digests and Defect Action Sheets; advisory material from key industrial authorities and key contractual documents.

Trade and professional journals pertaining to construction also have their uses. The entire range is too numerous to mention individually, but most libraries hold the prominent publications. Back copies are an excellent source of information, opinion, and trends (for example procurement lead-in times or cost indices in *Building* magazine).

There are also available a broad range of construction academic journals and these are a more reliable source of information. This is because the articles (papers) they contain are often refereed; that is, subjected to peer scrutiny before publication. Academic papers are normally well referenced and hence an excellent contributor to the desired 'snowball effect' of a literature search, introduced in Figure 2.5. earlier. Some of the most prominent academic construction journals are: *Construction Management and Economics*; and *Building Research and Information* published by E and FN Spon; *Building and Environment* published by Pergamon Press; and *Engineering, Construction and Architectural Management* published by Blackwell Science. The series of journals produced by *The American Society of Civil Engineers* (ASCE) is also well worth scrutiny (refer ASCE web address above).

Professional bodies such as the Chartered Institute of Building (CIOB) and the Royal Institution of Chartered Surveyors (RICS) will also provide literature searches of their own library stock. These are normally very detailed. My personal experience is that the CIOB search facility is particularly helpful. If you are not a member of these organisations; talk politely to someone who is, or arrange for student membership forthwith!

To summarise a literature search; get to know your library intimately, learn how to use it effectively, then put that acquired skill into practice. There is no substitute for stubborn persistence and avid legwork.

The assimilation of literature review information

From the above discussion it is clear that an adequate literature search will ultimately produce hundreds of items, (some will be more pertinent to your topic than others). To effectively assimilate this information requires a structured approach. To rely solely on memory and ad-hoc notes is unreliable. I recommend that both a system of information storage and the building of a word processed bibliographic listing are carried out. The information storage system can be used for identifying literature, and the listing for pasting relevant reference(s) into a document (e.g. dissertation or paper). I will discuss these each in turn.

Although we live in an age of advanced information technology, to develop the information store I advocate a simple manual index card system. This is because it is easy to compile and even easier to 'flick through' when searching for particular items either by keyword, title or author. A plastic index card holder, a copious amount of cards and some alphabetical dividers are all that is required. If however, you are totally committed to computerisation then such a system may be equally compiled on a suitable software package.

Whether you use cards or computer data base, the exact method of logging information is prone to personal taste. However, I will explain the system I use - it works perfectly for me.

Take a given piece of literature: this book for example. Assume we are to log this into the literature information store. On the face of a card, towards the top edge, is written the name and initials of the author(s). This needs to be near the top edge so that it is readily seen when the cards are searched through. (When the index card has been filled in, it will be filed in the card box in alphabetical order by author surname. So, this example will be placed under 'H').

Below the author name is written the year of publication followed by the title and nature of the material (e.g. book, journal, conference paper, etc.). Under this is inserted the name and location of the publisher. Finally, the bottom of the card displays other peripheral information such as the edition, ISBN / ISSN number, where obtained, number of pages, general availability and so on.

On the rear of the card (again towards the top edge for visibility) will be written a range of keywords, reflecting the salient aspects of the material. So in the case of this book these might be: built environment; research; thesis; dissertation; study; writing. Below this is written a brief description of the item for future reference. Figure 2.6 shows what the completed index card might look like. To file the literature in this way can be a little time consuming but, it will pay dividends throughout the research programme and beyond. For example, for further research or paper writing.

Once completed[4] the index box can scanned for three primary functions:

O   from the 'face side' when looking for work by a known author;
O   from the face side when looking for a precise title; or
O   from the 'reverse' when pursuing keyword(s).

Obviously there is little point in logging the literature in this way if an original copy of each item can not be found. A draw in a filing cabinet makes a perfect place for material such as copies of technical papers, to be stored either in alphabetical order or, by subject groups.

> TIP: careful logging of the literature and its safe storage can be time consuming, but will pay dividends later.

In tandem with the card index it is prudent to compile a word processed listing of the entire bibliography. This should be a list of all relevant literature, presented completely (see chapter four), and in alphabetical order. This bibliography will need to be typed up in any event, for the purposes of the reference list at the rear of a dissertation. So, if commenced early as advocated here, several advantages will evolve:

---

[4] The index will never be 'completed' as such, because new literature will constantly be uncovered.

Figure 2.6. Completed index card

HOLT, G. D.

1997 BOOK: A guide to successful dissertation study for students of the built environment.

Pub: The built environment research unit, University of Wolverhampton.

Loaned from institutional library .
Class no: XXX ISBN: 1 902010 00 0

Typical front view

KEYWORDS

Built environment research, thesis, dissertation, study, writing.

General description.

Book giving advice as to the pursuit of built environment dissertation study. Structure, research methodology, literature review, data analysis, editing, viva--voce

Typical rear view

○ typing the reference list is a tedious task and therefore prone to mistakes. Starting early means the task can be done in stages. This breaks the monotony so the list is less prone to error

○ any papers or articles written during the research will require a reference / further reading list. Once typed up, the computer bibliography can be copied and pasted into papers etc. at will, representing a time saving

○ fellow students may benefit from a copy of your bibliography. If working amongst a group of researchers, then such cross fertilisation of ideas and information will be beneficial to all.

The literature review write-up

Having performed the literature search and assimilated the material discovered, the 'results' of this exercise must be coherently written-up into the dissertation. This review write-up should not simply be a collection of quotes *verbatim*, but rather, a critique; that is, the contrasting of ideas and past and present thinking on the topic. This critique should serve as a vehicle for homing-in on the specific research objective(s).

The write-up should provide a context for the research. It should formulate questions and hypotheses and try to anticipate reader questions (e.g. what does *this* prove? What does *that* contrast show? What is the best way to solve *this* problem?). When writing the review constantly ask yourself: "Where is this taking me?" and "What am I ultimately leading up to?" My own experience is that many students fail to achieve such a critique but instead, believe that the citing of literature (almost at random) is adequate enough. In such cases what evolves is a text without direction. That is, the reader merely becomes consumed in a (well informed) novel, that leads to nowhere in particular.

The first thing required is a plan of direction; a 'micro' plan developed around the statements above: Where is this taking me and what am I ultimately leading up to? Using my favoured approach of an analogy, consider the review write-up as a funnel: into the top is poured a vast amount of literature containing empirical studies, data and postulation surrounding the topic. As this information runs down through the ever decreasing aperture of the funnel, consolidation is achieved. Out of the constricted lowermost part of the funnel comes a narrowed, well defined thinking, containing legitimate contentions and assertions for advancing the area of knowledge further. Figure 2.7. shows this analogy graphically.

The review write-up micro plan need be no more than a series of well thought out sentences offering a structure around which to write. As an example, let us assume that an undergraduate student has decided to investigate timber frame domestic housing. Then the review write-up micro-structure might be as follows:

○ brief comparison of domestic structural forms;
○ chronology of determinants on present day, favoured structural solutions;
○ the role of timber frame housing within that chronology;
○ current usage of timber frame housing; and
○ the student's assertions for future timber frame usage based on all the former.

This micro structure helps avoid the aimless wander referred to above. That is, the first point would introduce the reader to the entire range of domestic structural solutions (generate the context); the second point would identify key variables evolved over time that impact upon structural choice (cost, speed, insulation properties, aesthetic value etc.); the third point could put into perspective the role of timber frame in that evolution; the fourth would help make the discussion objective by introducing numeric data; and the last point would in essence be a summary based on what has gone before.

Here could also be the student's assertion or hypothesis for (say) future timber frame usage. This logical structure then somewhat automatically yields the prime research objective, which in this instance might be: "To investigate the potential, for timber frame usage in UK domestic housing construction, over the next 20 years".

Figure 2.7. Literature review: desired funnel effect

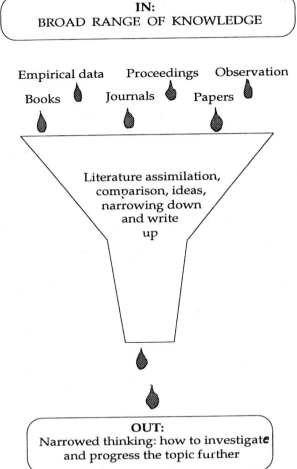

> TIP: be sure to develop a micro-plan around which to write your literature review.

I must at this point clarify as to how you should cite references within the narrative, in attempting to develop the desired critique. To continue the timber frame theme consider the following passage[5]:

Smith (1995) said: "timber frame is dead". This has been blamed on the construction process: "it is the construction process not the product, that causes problems" (Black, 1993). Jones (1994) said that: "timber frame has great potential". Some of this potential could be because of its insulation properties: "the energy savings because of increased insulation would be phenomenal" (Green, 1992).

Notwithstanding relevant quotes, this paragraph tells the reader little, it has no sense of destination. It also indicates that the student has not had (or used) an ability to synthesise the literature and develop a form of assertion or direction. For example, it could have been argued that the potential for timber frame housing exists but, that the reason the method is unfavoured is because of misconception:

At this time, timber frame usage for UK domestic dwellings is very limited. This situation has been reflected in the extreme view of Smith (1995) who stated that: "timber frame is dead". In contrast however, the potential offered by this form of construction has also been recognised (Jones, 1994). Indeed, it would seem that the negative aura surrounding timber frame is somewhat a function of misconception; the method itself may be sound; it is the UK climate (i.e. ingress of rainwater during construction) that generates complications: "it is the construction process, not the product that causes problems" (Black, 1993). Perhaps this situation could be addressed with stricter production practices, indeed, as White (1990) contends: "greater on-site management control is needed throughout the industry". Were this achieved, then maybe the benefits of; savings in national energy consumption via higher standards of insulation (Green, 1992); and reduction in harmful CO_2 outputs (Davis, 1990) might be realised.

---

[5] All references and statements cited are hypothetical for the purpose of this example.

The latter passage is longer but does reflect logical synthesis and reasonable assertion made by the student. This is the approach that must be aimed for in a successful review write-up.

Referencing the discussion

Referencing can, but need not, be a complex issue. My own experience is that students nearly always struggle to get it right. As with many other aspects of writing and style, flexibility exists but the fundamentals are carved in stone, as it were.

In the case of writing technical papers most journals have their own 'house style' and will require references to be cited using a particular method, and listed (within the bibliography) in a certain way. Alternatively, there are British (BSI, 1989) and International (ISO, 1987) standards that govern the task (see also Bosworth, 1995). However, for dissertation writing we can establish firm ground rules that adhere to recognised practice and make the referencing correct, but, do not over-complicate the issue!

The citing of references within a dissertation text (particularly within the literature review), can achieve several aims:

O   they can reinforce an argument or standpoint;
O   they can highlight contrasting views or contentions amongst the literature;
O   when comprehensive enough in number, they will show that a student has adequately researched (and hopefully read around) a subject; and
O   their use allows a reader to follow up specific aspects where required, that is, to obtain referenced material for their own use.

In striving to satisfy these aims, you may either:

O   directly quote someone, or something someone said / wrote e.g. Smith (1992) recommends that: "quote then given in inverted comma's here" or;

O   make a reference to someone or their work in a passive manner e.g. it has been indicated by Smith (1992) that. . .

Either way, the actual source of information, or contention cited, is important. The strongest source is from published material e.g. books or journals, particularly, refereed published work (i.e. from a journal that sends potential articles to experts in the field for refereeing: suitability, clarity, academic rigour etc. before acceptance for publishing). The other source is unpublished material such as in-house reports, face-to-face discussions or telephone conversations.

Try and use published material wherever possible because: i) of its reliability; ii) the fact that it is easier to reference; and iii) the reader can follow up the reference and obtain a personal copy if required. The use of unpublished material can cause problems, particularly: i) it is often more difficult to reference in the bibliographic list; and ii) you will probably need permission to cite it.

Regarding permission, treat all unpublished information as confidential unless you have (preferably written) permission to cite it. The only two sources that you are safe to cite without permission are public archives and theses (O'Connor, 1995 p80). Unpublished material that will require permission includes: private collection material; confidential material; material in preparation; informal or formal discussion or interview; telephone conversations; and technical reports.

If cited, unpublished material may be listed in the dissertation bibliography, or better still, within the text itself e.g. ". . . quote here" (telephone conversation with A.B. Smith of somewhere University, 14th December 1999).

Regarding method of referencing, there are two principal choices: the Harvard method and the sequential numbering (Vancouver) method.

The Harvard method

This is a system whereby each quote or reference is identified within the text by the author(s) surname and year of publication. For example:

> It has been stated that; "construction is a growing industry" (Smith, 1996).

This means that Smith has been quoted *verbatim* and, that the quote comes from material published in 1996. Alternatively, the source of information may be referred to in a passive sense like this:

> ... it was Smith (1996) that commented on the positive growth of the construction industry.

This means almost the same thing but the actual statement made by Smith has not necessarily been quoted verbatim. In the latter example, because the author's surname is used within the main text then only the year of publication need be given in parentheses. Smith is a common UK surname. Hence, if we have more than one Smith amongst the list of reference material (assume Michael Smith and Lisa Smith) then the appropriate one may be identified with an initial:

> ... it has been stated that; "construction is a growing industry" (Smith, M., 1996).

A further point of potential confusion, is where there are several sources of material amongst the references by the same author, that were published in the same year. If we assume two such sources by (say) Jones in 1996 then the first one may be designated an 'a' (or A) and the second a 'b' (or B) [third by 'c' and so on]. For example:

> Jones (1996a) originally reported a decline in demand, but has subsequently contradicted this by indicating an upturn (Jones, 1996b).

Where material is by more than one author, then up to and including three, are cited in the order that they appear on the title page of the material:

> "...quote" (Smith and Jones, 1997); or
> "...quote" (Smith, Jones and Evans, 1998).

Where more than three authors are on the literature title page, then it is normal to cite them all the first time the reference is given in the text:

> "...quote" (Smith, Jones, Evans and Black, 1998)

then to insert *et al* between the first author and year of publication thereafter:

> "...quote" (Smith *et al.*, 1998).

The *et al.* is Latin, meaning 'and others'. It can be used in the narrative, but the entire list of authors must be given under the bibliographic references list (see chapter four). If the author(s) is not identifiable (for example an anonymous article within a magazine), then "Anon" may be used:

> "Construction is a growing industry" (Anon, 1995).

In this instance the work will be included in the bibliographic reference list under Anon, followed by the year of publication and title of the article, then "IN:" followed by full journal details including page numbers (see below). The "IN" confirms that the article is in the cited journal. Hence, if the above was in *Building* magazine then the bibliographic entry would read:

Anon, (1995). "Title of article here". IN: Building magazine, Vol. CCLX, No. 13, p 7. London: The Builder group.

Where a particular chapter of a book is cited then this may be indicated as:

". . .quote" (Smith, 1996 chap 4).

A similar approach may be adopted for specific pages of the material:

". . .quote" (Smith, 1996 p 102).

In such instances a single p means one page i.e. page 102 in the above example. To cite several pages, pp is used hence, pp 102 - 106 means pages 102 to 106 inclusive.

There are methods of abridging a given reference for subsequent citing in a chapter. The three methods involve the Latin words: *idem* (someone previously mentioned); *ibid* (in the same place); and *op. cit.* (in the work cited). In text containing several references *idem* may be used to represent the author(s) of a second, or more items, following a previous reference by that author(s):

"construction is booming (Smith and Jones, 1996), particularly the refurbishment and road building sectors (*idem*, 1997).

So the article cited by Smith and Jones in 1997 contains the latter information. *Ibid* represents the entire same reference (author, title, volume etc.):

"construction is booming" (Smith 1996), . . ."second quote from Smith, 1996 here". . .(*ibid*).

Here, both quotes come from the one article. Where a subsequent reference to an earlier work is made but, other references have intervened in the text, then *op.cit.* may be used:

"quote from Smith 1996 here" (Smith, 1996). . .other text and references here. . . "second quote from Smith 1996 here" (Smith *op.cit.* p 99).

So page 99 of Smith (1996) houses the second quote. Where an original quotation is wrong in the sense that it (say) contains a typographical error then *sic* may be included in the quote in square brackets, to show the reader that the error appears in the original material:

> "The present growth in civil engineering and building projects is phenomenal, indeed construction is pooming [*sic*]" (Smith, 1996).

So it can be established that the current author has not spelled booming wrong! It is acceptable to cite several pieces of literature to reinforce one single point as follows:

> There has been much discussion of the role construction plays in the national economy (Smith, 1996; Jones, 1996a; 1996b; Smith *et al*, 1998).

All references cited using the Harvard method will be listed in alphabetical order; in the references list at the end of a dissertation. Hence, for the above paragraphs then the order will be: Black, Evans, Jones 1997a, Jones 1997b, Smith, L. and Smith, M. Chapter four explains in much more detail, how to list bibliographic information.

The sequential numbering (Vancouver) method

This is the other popular method of referencing. Quite simply, each different reference is given a unique number representing the order that it appears in the text. So the first reference will be [1], the second [2] and so on. If the first reference is subsequently cited, the number [1] will again be used. That is, you must regard the number as a unique identity for that reference alone, throughout the entire length of the chapter or the dissertation. The wording of the last sentence means that numbered references cited within the text, may be listed with all bibliographic details at the end of each chapter, or, at the end of a dissertation (explained in chapter four).

Unlike the Harvard system, bibliographic entries are listed in numerical order, not, alphabetical order. So if some of the previous authors were cited thus:

"quote from Black here" [1]. . .intervening text. . . "quote from Smith here" [2]. . .intervening text. . . "quote from Jones 1996a here" [3] . . .intervening text. . . "quote from Black again here" [1]. . .intervening text. . . "quote from Jones 1996b here" [4];

They would be listed in the references, in the following order: 1. Black; 2. Smith; 3. Jones 1996a; 4. Jones 1996b. The reference numbers do not have to be given in square brackets (although this is commonplace). Alternatively, they may be superscript numerals like this:

it has been stated that construction is booming[1]

or presented like this;

it has been stated that construction is booming [ref.1].

Multiple references are simply shown as:

. . .there has been much discussion of the role construction plays in the national economy[1,2,3,4] OR . . .economy [1, 2, 3, 4] OR . . . economy [refs 1 to 4].

Other less popular methods of referencing include: footnotes, hybrid alpha numeric and date order.

Footnotes use a superscript numeral after the quote like this[6]. Bibliographic details of each reference cited will be at the bottom of each page (see below) and on the same page as each respective reference appears. Some word processing packages have a footnote facility which automatically places the correct number in sequence within the text and, puts the footnote number under a line at the bottom of the page.

I would recommend that this method of referencing is avoided in a dissertation because it tends to make the pages look untidy, particularly where there are a lot of references cited.

---

[6] Corresponding bibliographic details would be given here.

Hybrid alpha-numeric referencing, first involves all references being listed in alphabetical order (as per Harvard system) and then each one being assigned a number in sequence (as per sequential numbering). When a reference is cited within the text, it is simply a case of using the corresponding number as determined from the list. This approach is also best avoided because the numbers within the text are not necessarily sequential: this seems to defy logic and may indeed cause confusion.

The date order method lists all references in the reference list, in (date) order of publication. To cite a reference, the date (vis-à-vis author and date) is given in the text similar to the Harvard system. Again, there seems little reason to use this approach and over-complicate the issue!

Confirming the dissertation objective(s)

It should be appreciated by now that if the literature review write-up has been conducted properly, then the research objectives (remember the question: What is this leading up to?) will almost evolve without conscious effort.

> TIP: Clearly identify your objectives in the introductory chapters so that the reader understands where you are going with the work.

The previous timber frame example can be used to confirm this. From the review evolved some fundamental issues including:

O   timber frame usage for domestic dwellings is limited at present;

O   increased timber frame usage could generate advantages for both its inhabitants and the environment.

It would be reasonable therefore (at first degree level) to formulate the prime dissertation objective as being: "to investigate why timber frame construction is perceived in such a bad light". This prime objective could be further decomposed into several groups of opinion (e.g. manufacturers, inhabitants, builders etc.). Were these opinions understood then perhaps insight for potential future acceptance of the timber frame method, could be determined. Hence, the aims may be confirmed as being to survey opinion of timber frame construction amongst three sub-samples of the overall sample; to contrast views between them, and to offer overall opinion and conclusions based on the aggregated survey.

Having narrowed down the topic, and confirmed the dissertation objectives, these must be written into the narrative so that the reader can identify exactly where the work is going. The next main component of a dissertation i.e. *The middle* can then be introduced within the text, by indicating as to how these aims might be satisfied.

This lead-in to the next section forms a link between components, as described in chapter one (also refer to Figure 1.3.).

Summary of the first component: The beginning

❏ The required dissertation format must be identified and adhered to: aim for simplicity, tidiness and consistency.

❏ Titles, headings and section numbers may all be provisionally decided upon as a means of establishing an overall dissertation structure.

❏ Be certain that the abstract accurately reflects the content of the dissertation and does not exceed one page in length. Include all necessary preliminary pages at the start of a dissertation.

❏ The first component (the beginning) of a dissertation will contain an introduction, the results of the literature review (critical discussion) and statement of objective(s) / hypotheses.

❑ The introduction should 'invite the reader in' and 'show the reader around' both the topic area and proposed dissertation structure.

❑ The literature review will consist of the information search; the assimilation and storage of material; and the review write-up. A wide variety of literature sources are available. Learn how to use these and the academic library, to full potential.

❑ All discussion, particularly the literature review, should be adequately referenced. The two prime methods of referencing are the Harvard method and sequential numbering. Use only one of these methods.

❑ The objective and aims of the dissertation should be made explicit early on. That way, the reader will know exactly where the work is heading.

Chapter three
Second component: The middle

This chapter explains the following points:

- ❑ how to choose a suitable research methodology
- ❑ points to consider when selecting a research sample
- ❑ points to consider with respect to surveys and experiments
- ❑ how to analyse your research
- ❑ how to present research findings

If everyone is thinking alike then somebody isn't thinking (General George Patton 1885-1945).

Introduction

The 'middle' component of a dissertation contains the actual 'nuts and bolts' of a research project. It should be original in terms of describing what was done, how it was performed, and the results obtained. The middle can adopt the following logical structure:

O   a description of the research methodology utilised and why chosen;

O   a description of how the research investigation (e.g. survey or experiment) was designed and conducted;

O   the analysis of research data; and

O   presentation and discussion of the most salient findings from such analysis.

This chapter discusses each of these components in this same order. It should be appreciated however, that in practice it is difficult to separate them in this way. They are all to some extent interrelated and therefore, can each impact upon others. For example, the research methodology utilised will in part be a function of defined objectives and the nature of available input (or resulting output) data. Alternatively, survey or experimental design, will be influenced in part by the overall methodology utilised and the required (i.e. most valid) forms of data analysis.

It is recommended that this chapter be read in its entirety to gain appreciation of these interrelationships. For the sake of readability, complex definitions of scientific methodology and operational research are purposely avoided; these specific issues may be followed up elsewhere if desired. In the first instance see: Preece (1994, chapters two and three); Rudestam and Newton (1992, chapter three); Leedy (1989); and Kidd (1989). To summarise, research methodology, experimental design, and data analysis can be very complex issues; this chapter serves to introduce the fundamental concepts. The student may then subsequently study in more detail those specific aspects relative to their dissertation.

Choosing the research methodology

Methodology is defined in the Collins English Dictionary as:

O   a system of methods and principles used in a particular
      discipline;
O   a branch of philosophy concerned with the science of method.

In the context of dissertation research, methodology may be perceived as the overall method applied to satisfy the aims of the investigation. Choice will primarily evolve from the specific research objective(s) and hence, cannot be totally resolved until the latter are firmly established (refer chapter two). Some understanding of the science of methods will help appropriate methodology selection. That is, we must consider the topic and the research objective(s), with respect to several characteristics.

These characteristics include:

- O   industrial / academic bias;
- O   conceptual / empirical requirements;
- O   qualitative / quantitative bias; and
- O   pure / applied bias.

Even these characteristics are to some extent interrelated! They will each now be discussed in turn.

> TIP: Choose a research methodology that will satisfy your objectives and fit into the overall framework of your dissertation. Don't choose a methodology *then* mould your dissertation around it.

Industrial / academic bias

Research is sometimes conducted to placate a purely industrial or commercial objective, being driven by a specific corporate aim e.g. to gauge consumer opinion with regard a new range of products. This form of research has little or no academic bias, and is beyond the remit of this book.

Research may be carried out in an academic environment, but, be instigated (often funded) by industry. This will also encompass a specific corporate aim. However, the design and approach to such work will normally be prone to flexibility and researcher discretion; often (but not necessarily) being performed by a student pursuing a higher degree. In this case, methodology will need to satisfy the research requirements of the degree being studied, whilst also facilitating tangible development in the topic area, as dictated by the needs of the industrial input.

Discrete academic research normally forms the basis, or part of, a degree. Here, methodology will primarily be a function of which (i.e. at what level) degree is being pursued. First degree dissertations often centre on process observation, measurement of opinion or qualitative survey. Degrees at Masters level will need to push frontiers a little further forward and so often adopt statistical or other analytical methods, in the development or testing of conceptual ideas. In-depth study of process and development of a new or revised concept would be typical for an MPhil, with structured survey; identification of key variables; and observation or measurement of process being acceptable research methods (explained in more detail later). At PhD level a contribution to knowledge is required of the work, so for example, any developed concept would need to be tested and validated. Mathematical modelling techniques are very often a feature of doctoral research.

TIP: Choose a methodology commensurate with the level of degree being studied.

Conceptual / empirical requirements

If the aim of your work is to cultivate a concept, then this will normally involve process observation and subsequent formulation of an abstract idea based typically on qualitative information. Conceptual research need not rely on experiment or experience and could be described as having a 'theoretical' bias.

In contrast, empirical research draws conclusions from more tangible, often numerical data or output. This is often the result of applying an input system(s) i.e. made up of 'independent' variables. (A more complete discussion of variables and other statistical issues follows later). Empiricism is the opposite of subjectivity and is closely allied to objectivity (Preece, 1994).

Alternatively, experimentation may be used to yield empirical data. Here it should be pointed out that experimentation is not necessarily a physical activity. For example, construction management research is in many ways a social science where experimentation will often be in symbolic or mathematical form. Either way, experimentation requires quantitative methodologies. In a symbolic context, computer simulation or advanced statistical techniques such as Multivariate Discriminant Analysis (cf. Kinnear and Gray, 1994) or Cluster Analysis (see Everitt, 1980) may be used. A mathematical model (revised / alternative model of the original process investigated -refer Figure 1.1.) normally ensues as a result of symbolic modelling.

Qualitative / quantitative bias

In research terms, a qualitative approach (methodology) means to utilise subjective methods very often based on personal opinion, perception, or feeling (i.e. quality). Process observation, opinion or expression, unstructured interview and open question surveys (see below), are synonymous with qualitative methods.

Quantitative methodologies involve consideration of size and magnitude and may be perceived as being more analytical in nature than qualitative methods. Structured interview, structured survey, symbolic models and physical experimentation, are all synonymous with quantitative methods.

Pure / applied bias

The main differences between pure and applied research were identified in chapter one. Based on that discussion and, what has been described above, we can now summarise that pure research will tend to:

O   be a feature of dissertations (vis-à-vis theses);
O   be associated with conceptual issues; and
O   rely more on qualitative methodologies, but quantitative studies are not excluded.

Applied research will tend to:

O   have a leaning toward some industrial / commercial application or bias;
O   be empirical in nature, and

O   utilise quantitative methodologies, but qualitative studies are not excluded.

Table 3.1. provides an overview of some specific methodologies applicable to each of the four aspects of research bias introduced above.

Table 3.1.

Indicative applications of some research methodologies with respect to four aspects of research bias

	Research bias			
Methodologies	Industrial (I) Academic (A)	Conceptual (C) Empirical (E)	Qualitative (Qt) Quantitative (Qn)	Pure (P) Applied (A)
Process observation	I A	C E	Qt	P
Process measurement	I A	E	Qn	A
Open question survey	A^1	C E	Qt	P
Structured survey	A^{1,2}	E	Qn	P A
Unstructured interview	A^1	C E	Qt	P A
Structured interview	A^{1,2}	C E	Qn	A
Symbolic experiment	A^{2,3}	C E	Qt Qn	P A
Physical experiment	A^{2,3} I	E	Qn	A
Mathematical model	A^3 I	E	Qn	A

KEY:

     A^1 = typically first degree level

     A^2 = typically masters degree level

     A^3 = typically doctoral research

Note: Table 3.1. is typical not definitive. For example, it is shown that mathematical models are used in both academic and industrial environments, typically for empirical work, of a quantitative nature, in an applied setting.

The methodologies cited are now briefly discussed in turn.

Process observation

Any hypothesised alternative or improvement to existing practice or knowledge, can not be properly considered, until the existing condition(s) and problems surrounding it, are fully understood. Much of this understanding will emanate from the literature search, but this in isolation will rarely suffice. A first and most simple complement to the literature search is observation. Observation alone may be considered as a qualitative methodology, yielding some understanding of the way a process or condition is conducted, or exists at present. In this context, process observation is most often recorded as a narrative (vis-à-vis numeric data).

An example of process observation is that of method study, this being a technique to record a procedure of work (Harris and McCaffer, 1989). Method study might initially be used for example, were a student concerned with construction productivity. Alternatively, where a dynamic situation exists then a series of observations may be required over time, prior to setting up a subsequent (say) field experiment(s) or data recording method(s). An example here might be description of an estuary at various times of the month or year prior to recording flow rates for wave power research.

Process measurement

This can take an inordinate number of forms but is essentially an extension of the latter method. To continue the productivity theme, then process measurement in this context could involve time study. Time study involves: i) familiarisation of the work; ii) collection of data by timing; iii) comparison of performance against accepted standards (if known); and iv) adjustment for effort and utilisation (see Pilcher, 1992 pp 198-228). Hence, (i) is an example of process observation and (ii) of process measurement.

Open question survey

Many aspects of built environment research utilise questionnaire surveys. The most straightforward of these is the open question survey. This employs a questionnaire inviting 'open' replies to the questions set. A typical open question might be:

"What is your opinion of the Latham recommendations with respect to dispute resolution?"

As can be appreciated, the biggest drawback with this approach is that theoretically there can be as many different responses as there are respondents! This type of qualitative research data can be more difficult to (objectively) analyse, albeit, there are ways to achieve this such as word counts (how many times did respondents use a particular key word) or, the grouping of 'like' answers (cf. Preece, 1994 pp 110-111). There are also software packages available designed to handle qualitative data so if you are considering open question surveys, it will be worthwhile finding out if such software is available to you.

> TIP: When deciding on a suitable research methodology consider what tools (e.g. software) are available to analyse your data.

Structured survey

Structured questionnaire survey is in effect, a more quantitative version of open question survey. An effective structured questionnaire requires meticulous planning and design. This design should anticipate:

O   the potential range of responses to questions (for the
         purpose of designing response / scoring categories); and
O   the necessary forms of data analysis that will be required
         for responses (refer to tip above).

If designed properly, structured questionnaire survey is a very effective means of performing quantitative research. A later section of this chapter: *Sampling, surveys and experimental design* will discuss in much more detail some of the processes involved in a questionnaire survey.

Unstructured interview

This can be perceived as the oral equivalent of process observation. Essentially, being unstructured (i.e. no preconceived format) it is a means of abstracting qualitative information. For example, qualitative attitude measurement. The former question about Latham's recommendations under *open questionnaire* above, could be a suitable opening question for an unstructured interview. Thereafter, the interview might take any direction this depending primarily upon the knowledge, strength of opinions, and character of the interviewee (and interviewer for that matter!).

Notwithstanding there being no defined interview format, an interviewer will normally have some preference for which direction the interview should take. Very often this will be implicit and therefore, s/he should be mindful of such feelings not being allowed to influence the discussion for it to remain truly 'unstructured'. Any interference by the interviewer in this respect can lead to bias in the answers provided.

Structured interview

Here, the interview follows a predetermined route. It involves the interviewer using a standard set of questions designed to influence the direction of discussion. The process should emphasise objectivity, uniform treatment of all interviewees, and avoidance of any other possible external influences (see Preece, 1994). That way, interviews may be analysed on a 'like-for-like' basis and therefore, the method may be perceived as being more objective than the unstructured technique.

Interviews are best recorded for later typing-up of transcripts where necessary (e.g. they may form appendices within a dissertation). Further, the transcript may be required for analysis purposes using software packages like that described earlier. One such package is NUD.IST; this being designed to analyse any kind of qualitative data whether textual or not. Analysis can not properly be performed on notes and / or memory alone.

An example of a technique to conduct quantitative analysis of interviews will be found in Humphries (1994). See also Hannagan (1986, pp 257-8). Humphries used *content analysis* to draw inferences from interview data. This involved calculating: the time allocated by an interviewee towards a given subject; total words spoken with respect to a subject; and word counts expressed in relative terms i.e. percentage of total interview. This is a perfect example of applying quantitative analysis to what is essentially a qualitative methodology.

Symbolic experiments

These are performed using symbolic models. That is, models which represent or typify something. Symbolic models take many forms e.g. a verbal symbolic model could be a specification or other 'binding' or 'controlling' document. However, in the context of research, symbolic models are those which represent a situation or sequence of events but not in a physical form. (The latter are physical experiments). Typically, symbolic experiments use a system of mathematical equations (see Kidd, 1989). We may put symbolic models into perspective, with a typical example.

A fundamental task of the construction manager is that of decision making. Invariably, this involves the consideration of a decision option with respect to several (decision) criteria. If we:

O   designate the ultimate decision choice (the decision option) as being the dependent variable, that is, it is dependent upon 'other' factors; and

O   designate the influencing factors (the decision criteria) as being independent variables, that is, they are independent of the dependent variable;

Then the decision task may be modelled symbolically using a mathematical equation such as a multiple regression function (explained later).

That is the theory, but where does research come into all of this? Well, let us further assume that the above management decision was: "To select an appropriate corporate strategy with respect to company growth over the next three years". The literature search would indicate, amongst other things, possible independent variables to be considered. These could include: existing and historical company turnover figures; current and previous profit margins; predicted demand; current and predicted market forces and so on.

Data collection might involve the accumulation of financial accounts for a sample of companies exhibiting varying degrees of growth over a defined period. By analysing the characteristics of this sample with respect to each independent variable and, subsequently regressing the values of the independent variables onto the dependent variable (i.e. actual growth achieved), then a symbolic model would be derived. I have described this in a simplistic manner; in practice it is not quite so simple. For example, when using multiple regression the measurement of independent variables should ideally be at the interval level (see *Analysing the research* later) and this is not always easily achieved.

The derived symbolic model would then be 'tested' by applying it to real life situations. That way, output of the model (which would be predicted growth i.e. the dependent variable), may be compared with actual growth achieved. Were significant correlation to exist between predicted and actual (growth) then we would say that the symbolic model has been 'validated'. In this context significant is normally taken to mean correct in 95 out of 100 cases and validation means to test or prove that something actually works as planned.

Physical experiments

These are the 'tangible' equivalent of symbolic experiments and tend to represent, model, or test physical phenomenon. A perfect example would be the construction of a scale model bridge, to test a new or alternative design, or alternative materials.

You should be mindful that physical experiments can be time consuming to design, conduct, record and analyse. Hence, they are discussed in greater detail later.

Mathematical models

These need only be seriously considered for dissertations at Masters level and above. Mathematical models tend to deal with quantitative data and typically aim (but are not limited) to either:

O   test a course of action(s) e.g. predict an outcome;
O   classify an item(s); or
O   identify a best option from amongst a range of alternatives.

The earlier example of a symbolic model (company growth) was also a mathematical model (it tested a course of action based on quantified input variables and predicted an outcome). Here then is an example of the overlap mentioned at the outset of this chapter i.e. a mathematical, symbolic model.

To discuss all possibilities with respect to mathematical models would require a volume larger than this book! However, you might wish to follow-up the subject with any of the wealth of books available on modelling and operational research. In the first instance see: Kidd, (1989); French *et al*, (1986); Wilkes, (1989); Hillier, (1990); Littlechild and Shutler, (1991); Urry (1991); and Taha, (1992).

> TIP: The rigorous use of an appropriate research
> methodology is a characteristic of successful
> dissertations.

Sampling, surveys and experimental design

The theory of samples and surveys is most easily understood in terms of three definitions:

Population. A population is <u>all</u> of the items conforming to a given set of criteria. For example, the population of UK civil engineering contractors (i.e. regardless of company size) amounts to thousands of such firms. However, the population of UK civil engineering contractors with an annual turnover in excess of £10M is smaller, whilst a similar population with a turnover in excess of £100M would be smaller still. Therefore, the parameters that define a population will include or exclude certain items and hence, dictate population size.

Sample. A sample is a limited number of items selected from a population. If a population contains 1,000 items (e.g. contractors above) then we might select say ten per cent of that population for examination. So in this case the sample would contain 100 items. In statistical terms, the number of items in a sample are often referred to as 'n' (i.e. in this example n = 100).

Survey. Having identified a sample then the items selected may be surveyed or otherwise examined (e.g. tested if we were looking at the strength of a material). This is so that we may observe trends or, draw conclusions <u>about the population</u>; but based on <u>information from the sample.</u>

It can be appreciated therefore, that a sample (in contrast to a population) is identified and surveyed for several reasons:

O   Time. It takes less time to survey a (smaller) sample than it would an entire population.
O   Cost. In view of the above it therefore costs less also.
O   Practicality. It may be inordinately difficult (indeed impossible) to identify and survey every member of a population.
O   Destructive analysis. Some tests may be destructive in nature and hence it would be impractical to test (destroy)

every item of a population.

O   Statistical laws. Survey of a sample can predict with a known degree of accuracy certain aspects of the population. That is, there is no need to survey an entire population to draw such conclusions.

There are many sampling methods, each designed to achieve certain objectives. We will consider:

O   simple random sampling;
O   stratified random sampling;
O   systematic sampling; and
O   quota sampling.

Simple random sampling

The theory behind this method is that every item of the population has an equal probability of being selected for the sample. Typically, random numbers are used to select items. True random numbers can be taken from statistical tables or generated on scientific calculators, or statistical software. Hence, if the population are each assigned a unique number $(1,2,\ldots N$; where N = population size) then, items corresponding to the random numbers may be drawn from the population until the required sample size (n) is achieved. The advantage of this method is that it is simple to perform. The disadvantage is that it can generate sample bias. For example, using the civil engineering contractor scenario earlier, then what is to say that the chosen sample will contain only firms from a certain geographical region or firms of a particular size? If this was the case then such a sample is not *representative* of the population; it is said to be *biased*. Biased samples produce biased inferences.

Stratified random sampling

Here, the population is firstly classified into mutually exclusive strata and the sample randomly drawn from these strata in such a way as to include proportionate amounts of each. For example, the civil engineering contractor population could be classified in terms of the following strata: small contractors; large contractors; general civil engineering firms; and specialist firms. Using stratified random sampling, we would then randomly select an equal proportion of each classification and our sample might be made up of 120 contractors as follows:

	General contractors	*Specialist contractors*
Small contractors	30	30
Large contractors	30	30

The philosophy behind stratified sampling is that it offsets the potential for bias associated with simple random sampling.

Systematic sampling

As the name implies, with this method the sample is systematically drawn from the population. This is normally achieved by selecting every mth item. Hence, if we were investigating a population of 2,000 items and required a 10 per cent sample then every 10th item of the population would be systematically selected.

Quota sampling

This is similar in many respects to stratified random sampling, but it is non-random. Rather, it is 'representative' sampling. First, the population is characterised in view of certain criteria, then representative sub-samples consisting of these characteristics make up the entire sample. This is best understood by example. Quota sampling is often associated with (but not exclusive to) interview surveys. Having identified the characteristics required (e.g. age group; social class; salary band etc.) then the first items (individuals) randomly encountered that meet these characteristics, are included in the sample (interviewed). This is why interviewers on the high street (for example at election time) ignore some people and purposely target others.

Required size of sample

It is generally accepted in statistical terms, that the larger a sample, then the more reliable are the results (inferences) drawn from tests performed upon it. However, gains in reliability of the output of statistical tests are not necessarily proportional (i.e. linear) to increases in sample size. For example, an increase in sample size by a factor of nine is required to divide the standard error by three (standard error is a measure which indicates the reliability of sample means with respect to estimated population means).

To put it another way, an increase in sample size from 50 to 20 000 is necessary to reduce chance fluctuations in results of analysis, by only a factor of 20 (Freund and Simon, 1992).

A simple rule of thumb is this: the more homogenous a population then the smaller that samples can be (drawn from it), and vice-versa. Therefore, sample size is a judgement based on the amount of variability that is known to exist within the population. Another 'general' rule is that minimum sample size should be 30. There are methods of calculating sample size to achieve given levels of confidence for sample means, such methods being discussed in most statistical texts. In the first instance read up on *confidence limits.*

> TIP: Ensure your research sample is well designed in terms of stratification and size.

Surveys

As earlier indicated, questionnaire surveys are very useful in built environment research. However, the correct design of questionnaires is critically important and can be a complex issue. I could not adequately cover this subject in a book of this nature so for this reason, some background reading on the subject is strongly recommended before undertaking such a survey. The social science section of an academic library is the best starting point. However, some basic but important principles are given:

O   Do not survey for survey sake. Understand why you are initiating the survey and exactly what you are trying to achieve. Are you asking the right questions to satisfy your research objectives? A smaller, initial 'test survey' (known as a pilot survey) can be useful in this respect.

O   Survey response data is only as reliable as the sample composition and size from which it emanates, so understand the preceding section of this book. Sample design is as important as questionnaire design.

O   Keep questionnaires as short as possible. A long questionnaire is more prone to rejection and hence will often achieve a lower response rate. Further, a respondent will lose interest towards the end of a long questionnaire and tend to treat the questions in a cursory manner.

O   To encourage responses always enclose a stamped, addressed reply envelope with your questionnaire and a brief, explanatory covering letter.

O   The initial component of a questionnaire should outline BRIEFLY the survey purpose, who is conducting it, and why.

O   Confidentiality of responses should be made explicit.

O   A section should be included in the questionnaire to allow classification of responses. That is, obtain information such as who completed the questionnaire, type of respondent, location of respondent, etc. Personal questions such as 'name of respondent' should be optional.

O   The main data collection section should be well designed in terms of "how will I analyse this data when collected?" Structure the questions in such a way that required analyses can be applied to the data (see *Analysing the research* later).

O   Always include your name and address at the end of the questionnaire. Remember that the questionnaire and the covering letter you send with it, might become separated by the recipient.

O   Be professional. Use a high quality paper, a laser printer to produce originals for photocopying purposes and clear unambiguous text. Always thank the respondent for taking part.

It is worthwhile if not courteous, to indicate <u>exactly</u> how you would like the respondent to answer your questions. This is best achieved by showing a simple example like so:

Please indicate your response to the following statements, by circling the number that best reflects your level of agreement. For example, if you strongly disagree then:

Strongly agree		Neither agree nor disagree		Strongly disagree
1	2	3	4	(5)

In summary, questionnaires should be adequately thought out, meticulously designed and well presented, to a carefully selected sample.

Design of physical experiments

I am indebted to my colleague Dr D. Halsey for compiling this section. *'A sceptical attitude lies at the root of all good experimental work, and should be consciously cultivated'* (Wood and Martin, 1974, p3). In many scientific and engineering disciplines, physical experimentation is the major research methodology. Most students on built environment courses will be required to conduct some scientific study (e.g. construction materials or environmental engineering). If your work involves experimentation then proper experiment design is an essential part of a successful dissertation. The importance of experimental design increases greatly as one moves from first degree (e.g. BSc) through masters level (e.g. MSc) to

PhD level. At first degree level, methodologies are generally obtained from relevant text books, laboratory manuals, or British Standards. At PhD level, an advancement to current knowledge is required. Very often it is necessary to develop the experimental technique(s) in itself, in order to achieve this advancement. Therefore, at PhD level, experimental design is of critical importance.

Experiments may be conducted in a laboratory (e.g. compressive strength testing) or in the field / on site (e.g. survey and measurement of dry rot). In many instances physical experiments rely on both field *and* laboratory techniques. For example, a student studying the deterioration of a construction material may decide to make detailed measurements of the material *in-situ* e.g. as part of a building. However, it may also be necessary for a sample of the material to be taken back to the laboratory for analysis or to simulate the deterioration processes. Simulations are often conducted in the laboratory because they offer controlled conditions. It is this 'control' offered by laboratory experiments, combined with the realistic conditions offered by field work, that often creates a need for both forms of experimentation to be utilised simultaneously, in order to satisfy a research aim.

If we continue with our example of researching the cause of deterioration of a construction material, then typical field work may include detailed measurement of the conditions to which the material has been exposed, e.g. temperatures (see Halsey, 1996). This may lead to the hypothesis that fluctuations in temperature cause the deterioration of the material. In the field it is impossible to isolate temperature changes from other factors (such as rainfall), so this hypothesis would be difficult to test. However, if the material is taken to the laboratory then controlled conditions would allow it to be exposed to temperature fluctuation only. In some instances simultaneous interactions between several variables are impossible to avoid. This situation results in more than one variable having an impact upon the test at the same time. Alternatively, it may be hypothesised that simultaneous variations in the variables are important and require studying.

Returning to our example, it may be hypothesised that fluctuations in temperature <u>and</u> moisture have a combined effect, in causing the deterioration of the material. This situation is dealt with by employing a statistical design to find the effects of each variable. Cox (1958) provides more information on statistical design in this context.

In a similar manner to surveys, practical experimentation must only be conducted once it is clear what the experiment is designed to achieve. Experimental studies require important variables to be identified and an experiment designed to establish their effect. This can be difficult to achieve and if experimental work is to be successful it must be very carefully planned. Furthermore, the data derived from an experiment are only as reliable as the experimental methods included in the design. For more information on experimental error, dealing with error, and precision, refer to Brinkworth (1973).

Experimental design is a crucial stage in any research project and considerable time should be spent on this activity. The design ultimately determines if the research aims will be met, and to what degree of efficiency and accuracy. Because physical experiments are often time consuming and require considerable equipment they must be designed carefully, in particular, ensuring that equipment, finances and time are adequately available for completion. Many students underestimate the time needed to conduct experiments. Consequently, they are unable to complete the analysis of experimental data and incorporate this into the dissertation. This obviously has disastrous effects because it is ultimately the write-up of experiments that examiner(s) assess. Again, in a similar way to surveys the design of experiments must consider what type of data will be generated. Understanding the *nature* of experimental data and how it should be analysed must be appreciated at the design stage (see *Analysing the Research* later). This is important because generally, data analysis utilises statistical tests which require certain criteria to be met. If this is not appreciated then data analysis may not be correct, or as complete, as was initially thought possible.

Once an experiment has been designed it is usually necessary to conduct a pilot study in the laboratory or field. This is to see if the methodologies devised are workable and likely to meet the research aims. However, it is also worth noting that even complete and thorough experimental design can not account for all eventualities. When conducting research, especially at PhD level, the results may not represent what was expected. Therefore, the experimental design may have to be altered en-route, to account for a new lead that may improve the chances of meeting the research aims. As a result, experimental design should be thought of as an ongoing process, asking questions along the way, and not proceeding to the next step until you have all the answers. Therefore, whilst conducting experiments it is very common to 'fine tune' an experimental design. It is essential that a record of this fine tuning is kept alongside the results from each experiment. To do this, a log book of the experiments should be meticulously maintained. In my own experience it is best to use hardback notebooks, one for field work, and one for laboratory work. It is also advisable to extract the data from the log books as soon as possible and back them up on computer (see *Chapter 2*). Becoming conditioned to this is essential to limit the chances of data loss.

In summary, like so many other aspects of research the *correct design* of physical experiments is critical. Most academic libraries contain numerous books on the design of experiments for each specific scientific and engineering discipline. I strongly recommend that students consult such books for the particular discipline under study, prior to commencing any physical experimentation.

> TIP: Be aware that physical experimentation requires meticulous planning, accurate recording of the data and can be more time consuming than might at first be realised.

Analysing the research

Analysis is intrinsically linked to other aspects of the research and hence, will be a function of satisfying research objectives, the nature of the research methodology employed and nature of data generated (e.g. from observation, experiment etc.). Research data analysis is essentially an exercise in observing numbers and hence tends to revolve around statistics. Experience has demonstrated to me that this characteristic of dissertation compilation either 'makes or breaks' a student's work. That is, a basic grasp of statistics is a prerequisite to almost any successful dissertation. The correct choice of analysis is important because:

O wrong analysis will inevitably lead to wrong conclusions (generally termed statistically as *inferences*) and /or;
O important conclusions may go undetected and / or;
O incorrect conclusions may be drawn.

Combined or singularly, if the above hold true then the research will not be exploited to its full potential, or even worse, will be fundamentally wrong. This is not a book about statistics. However, in view of the important link between this branch of mathematics and successful dissertation compilation I will now explain some basics (key words are highlighted in italics). A student already versed in statistics may skip this section. Alternatively, the book by Ruddock (1995) provides an excellent introductory text, particularly, in that it deals with statistics in a built environment context.

TIP: Analysis requires that you have a fundamental grasp of statistics. Limit your analysis to suit your abilities.

Types and measurement of data

Before any analysis can take place, the research data must be understood. Only when the nature of a data set are recognised can the correct analyses be applied to it. Research normally revolves around three classes of data:

O nominal data (descriptive e.g. minor road; major road; motorway);
O ordinal data (ranks e.g. 1st; 2nd; 3rd);
O interval data (numeric e.g. on a scale of 1 to 5).

Further classifications exist but are beyond the scope of this book.

Nominal data tend to be qualitative in nature and facilitate category membership. To use the company growth scenario presented earlier, then in collecting data the researcher will record discrete categories e.g. nature of company activity, geographical location, etc. Subsequently these nominal data may be used to classify the entire original sample into subsequent sub-samples e.g. national contractors, national speculative builders, national civil engineers, 'local' contractors and so on. Such classification is useful in segregating a large original data set, prior to applying more numerical statistical tests or analyses between the resulting sub-samples.

Ordinal data are quantitative in nature and qualify members of the data set in terms of being larger / smaller, greater / lesser. Most often, this is used as a means of assigning order (e.g. ascending) or, ranks to the set. The use of ranks in research analysis can be very useful, for example, in terms of observing correlation between sub-sets or even for hypothesis testing. An excellent description of such analyses may be observed in Meddis (1984). As a practical example, a student investigating preference or opinion via structured questionnaire survey might use ordinal sorting of the resulting data set, based on the aggregated said preferences or opinions.

Interval data is also quantitative and involves the measurement of variables on an independent scale with equal units of measurement. For example, a questionnaire survey might have requested 'scoring' of the above mentioned preference or opinion on a scale of say one to seven. These 'opinions' represent interval data. The main failing of interval data is that it often has an arbitrary zero and hence the number 30 assigned to a variable does not necessarily mean that it represents twice the characteristic of another variable assigned 15. Where a 'true' zero does exist then this is *ratio measurement* i.e. assignment of zero to a variable represents absence of the quantity being measured, whilst 30 represents exactly twice as much of the quantity as does a value of 15.

Having briefly discussed the nature of data we will now consider analysis of data sets in terms of:

O   data exploration; and

O   tests on or amongst the data.

Prior to performing any tests on data set(s) (e.g. to look for significant differences between the sets of opinion above), it is useful to first investigate the raw data itself to understand its nature. This is because certain characteristics of the data may preclude it from, or make it particularly suitable for, a particular test later.

> TIP: Understand the nature of your data before attempting particular statistical tests upon it.

Data exploration

Quantitative data is a collection of numerical values. Many exploratory investigations may be performed on a data set and although they are often relatively simple, these initial investigations can yield much insight. We will consider data exploration in terms of:

O   central tendency;

O   dispersion;

O   variability;

O   skewness; and

O   confidence limits.

Central tendency is a generic term representing the 'central' characteristics of a data set and is normally represented by either: the arithmetic mean, the median or the mode.

The arithmetic *mean* ($\bar{x}$) of a variable x, is most commonly used. This being simply the sum of individual values within the set; divided by the number of cases or items (designated n). The biggest drawback of this measure is that extreme (high or low) values within the set will influence the mean and the result may not be truly representative (i.e. 'central'). In statistics such extreme values are termed *outliers*. The influence of outliers can lead to unrepresentative inferences.

The *median* is the middle item of a set of data. That is, if the data are arranged in numerical rank order (smallest item to largest item) then the middle value (or where the data set is an even number then the sum of the middle two values divided by two) is the median. The median is not so prone to influence by outliers as is the arithmetic mean.

The *mode* is quite simply the value occurring most frequently in the set. Where all values are different then the set is said to be *non-modal*. Where two groups of values occur most frequently then the set is said to be *bi-modal*. Where several groups of values occur most frequently then the set is said to be *multi-modal* and hence, there is no <u>single</u> typical value.

These three measures of central tendency are demonstrated in Table 3.2., which is a data set recorded from a survey of 30 speculative builders. They were each asked to record how many houses they had built during the last financial year.

As can be seen, the (arithmetic) mean number of houses built is 52, whilst the median value is 41. No single mode value exists so the data set is said to be multi-modal.

Investigation of *dispersion* shows how tightly the data are distributed about its mean value. This is important, because when the data are more dispersed then the less representative are its measures of central tendency (and vice-versa). The most simple measure of dispersion is *the range*: this being the difference between the smallest and largest values. For the above example then range is 290 - 0 = 290.

A more meaningful and common measure of dispersion is the *sample standard deviation* (designated s). The smaller the value of the standard deviation, then the more tightly the data are distributed and vice-versa. I purposely avoid the formula and calculations: every statistical package or even calculator will do this for you.

In the above example s = 54.4 houses. This is a relatively high value and is influenced by the extreme values within the set (case number 14 with a value of 290 must have been a larger builder, or one who built only houses; whilst two of the sample i.e. cases 9 and 13 built no houses at all). These extreme values are non-representative and will, for the purposes of this discussion, be classed as outliers. If we remove these extremes then the arithmetic mean is 47.10 and s becomes 29 (i.e. the data is now more tightly dispersed about $\bar{x}$).

Table 3.2.

Number of houses built by a sample of 30 builders during one financial year

Item No. (n)	Item Value (x)	Item No. (n)	Item Value (x)	Item No. (n)	Item Value (x)
1	12	11	64	21	17
2	20	12	80	22	106
3	37	13	0	23	50
4	106	14	290	24	10
5	18	15	84	25	38
6	57	16	18	26	42
7	62	17	40	27	60
8	5	18	62	28	19
9	0	19	30	29	75
10	70	20	10	30	80

Mean = $(\Sigma x) \div n = 1562 \div 30 = \underline{\underline{52.067}}$

Median = item $(n + 1) \div 2 = (30 + 1) \div 2 = 15.5$th item. So if data are then arranged in ascending order, then because data set is an even number we add items number 15 and number 16 and divide by 2. That is, $[(40 + 42) \div 2] = \underline{\underline{41.00}}$

Mode = most frequent value. Because this data set contains: 2 x zero, 2 x 10's, 2 x 18's, 2 x 62's, 2 x 80's, and 2 x 106's then it is said to be multi-modal.

Variability is another observation on dispersion. The prime disadvantage of the standard deviation is that it is expressed in natural units (in the foregone example, number of houses). We can convert this absolute measure of dispersion into a relative measure termed the coefficient of variation (designated cv). That is, express the sample standard deviation as a percentage of the sample arithmetic mean via the formula:

$cv = s \div \bar{x}$, where; $\bar{x}$ = sample mean.

The result may be expressed as a decimal or multiplied by 100 and expressed as a percentage. So for our original standard deviation example above then: $cv = 54 \div 52 = 1.03$. If we calculate cv after the removal of outliers then: $cv = 29 \div 47 = 0.61$; i.e. dispersion around the sample mean is 61 per cent. It is clear therefore, that the larger the value of cv then the more dispersed are the data about their mean value.

Skewness measures the degree of asymmetry of the distribution of a data set. The existence of several extreme values will cause a distribution to be 'skewed' in one direction or the other. The effect of this skewness is to pull the sample mean value, in one direction or the other, and thereby produce a non representative (i.e. either too large or too small) mean value for that data set. In view that for a normal i.e. symmetric distribution, the arithmetic mean, the median and the mode all coincide, a skewness coefficient expresses this relationship (displacement of the median from the mean) in relative terms. This is achieved via the formula:

Skewness = 3(mean - median) $\div$ s; where skewness is a coefficient in the range -3 to 3, with zero representing symmetry.

For the earlier examples then with outliers: $(3(52 - 41)) \div 54 = 0.6$; so the data is positively skewed. If we remove the outliers then: $(3(47 - 42)) \div 29 = 0.5$; so the data has become less skewed.

Positive skewness means that a smaller portion of large positive scores in the data set tend to produce a non representative (larger) arithmetic mean, whilst negative skewness has the opposite affect.

Confidence limits indicate how representative a sample mean value is, with respect to the population from which the sample was drawn. That is, the above sample of builders (n = 30) was randomly drawn from a population of many thousands of builders, but how representative is the sample mean ($\bar{x}$ = 52) of the population mean? (Population mean is designated μ and pronounced "mu"). To investigate this, 95 per cent confidence limits (CL) may be calculated from:

CL = $\bar{x}$ $\pm$1.96 ($\sigma \div \sqrt{n}$); where σ = standard deviation <u>of the population</u> and n = sample size.

(Population standard deviation (σ) is pronounced "sigma"). The 1.96 is a constant that gives 95 per cent confidence that the population mean (μ) will fall between the upper and lower CLs. For samples such as the above where n $\geq$ 30 then a normal (i.e. symmetrical) distribution may be assumed (Freund and Simon 1992) and hence, (because the population standard deviation σ is not available) the sample standard deviation (s) may be used in the formula instead. Having calculated the standard error then $\bar{x}$ $\pm$ this confidence interval (as it is known) gives predicted population mean range.

For our original sample of 30 builders then: CL = $\bar{x}$ $\pm$1.96 (54.4 $\div \sqrt{30}$) = $\bar{x}$ $\pm$19.46 so there is 95 per cent confidence that the population mean (μ) should fall between: (52 - 19.46) = 32.54 and (52 + 19.46) = 71.46 houses. Having removed the outliers then: CL = $\bar{x}$ $\pm$1.96 (29 $\div \sqrt{27}$) = $\bar{x}$ $\pm$10.93 so there is 95 per cent confidence that μ should fall between: (47 - 10.93) = 36 and (47 + 10.93) = 58 houses. Removal of the outliers has therefore reduced the range of the 95 per cent CLs, but because n is now < 30 then s is no longer reliable (i.e. a larger sample should have been surveyed!).

Tests on or amongst the data

The potential here is tremendous! A vast array of specialist books are available describing statistical and other mathematical tests or predictive algorithms. Hence, I present only an overview of the basic principles. We will consider tests on data in terms of:

○   comparing means of data sets;
○   investigating association between data sets;
○   statistical prediction; and
○   multivariate statistics.

It is re-emphasised that the following is but a guide: you should consult a detailed statistical text to completely understand any of the techniques discussed, before employing them (Ott, 1993 is a good starting point).

Comparing means

Often, data sets will need to be compared to confirm whether the arithmetic means of each set are significantly different from each other. For example, a survey may have investigated opinion between (say) two sub-groups, namely, Architects and Structural Engineers -such opinion having been measured via numerical scoring. The research question might be: "With respect to the question answered, are the resulting mean scores *significantly* different between these two sub-groups?" The word significant is important. In statistical terms one is able to set a significance level (normally 95 per cent or 99 per cent). Should the test accept that there is a difference at say the 95 per cent level, then this means that we can accept this finding with 95 per cent confidence (such a probability level may also be expressed as $p \leq 0.05$). At the 99 per cent level ($p \leq 0.01$) the result is even more robust.

For interval data the most common test for comparing means in this way is the *t-test*. The *independent samples t-test* is used where no relationships exist amongst the data sets, that is, they are totally independent of each other (as in the above Architect / Engineer example). Where a relationship does exist (e.g. a single data set is being tested for difference between responses to two different questions) then the *paired samples t-test* will be applied. It is critically important to establish whether or not the samples are related, and apply the correct t-test.

Caveat: before applying the t-test, the data sets should be investigated for *normality*. If the data are not 'normally distributed' then the t-test should not be applied, but rather, a *non-parametric* equivalent should be used. See Kinnear and Gray (1995) for expansion on this important point.

Where the data are ordinal, then differences amongst mean values of independent samples (or sub-groups) may be investigated with the *Mann-Whitney test*. If the data are ordinal but the samples are in some way related (e.g. as per in the t-test description above) then the *Wilcoxon test* is suitable. For nominal data the *Chi-square test* can investigate independent samples and the *McNemar test* related samples.

The forgone assumes that there are two sets of data only. However, where more than two sets (groups) exist then an *Analysis of Variance* (ANOVA) test may be used. ANOVA evaluates the between-groups variability against within-groups variability to compute a significance test (hypothesis) that the means of the groups are not all the same. If ANOVA does discover a difference between means of the groups, then a *post-hoc* comparison of means must be performed to identify exactly where these differences are (i.e. between which groups). This post-hoc test is performed because the ANOVA will only confirm that the means of several sets or groups are not the same, it will not confirm exactly where such differences exist.

Investigating association between data sets

The above tests generally sought to investigate significant difference between data sets. Levels of association between sets may be thought of as the opposite to this. For example, using the former Architect / Engineer scenario then assume these two groups were asked to rank in order of importance ten factors impacting upon buildability of design. Investigation of level of association between these rankings would confirm, or otherwise, whether Architects and Engineers agreed on the ten factors presented to them. In this context, statistical significance takes on the same meaning as described earlier.

Level of association is more commonly described as the *degree of correlation* (represented by a number termed the correlation coefficient). Correlation can be positive (+) or negative (-). A correlation coefficient has an absolute range of 0 to 1.0 where zero represents no correlation at all and 1.0 represents perfect correlation. Therefore, a correlation coefficient of 0.9 would mean that in the above example, both Architects and Engineers expressed a high level of agreement in ranking ten factors that impact upon buildability of design. A negative coefficient e.g. -0.9 would confirm the opposite: i.e. factors ranked high priority by the one group were ranked low priority by the other.

A few words of caution: care must be taken as not to confuse association and causation. That is, a high level of association between a variable(s) does not automatically mean that one is the cause of the other(s). Furthermore, investigation of correlation should be complemented wherever possible with a scatterplot. An excellent description of this rationale is given in Kinnear and Gray (1995 pp 154-5).

The above example (i.e. ranks: ordinal data) would be investigated for association with the *Rank Spearman correlation test*. Where the ordinal data sets are small, and contain joint rankings then *Kendall's tau* would be more robust than Spearman. Interval data would be investigated using the *Pearson correlation test*. Alternatively, two sets of nominal data can be explored for existence (but not strength of) of correlation using the *Chi-square statistic*.

Statistical prediction

To expand in a particular direction the 'level of association' theme, it can be useful in terms of research to be able to predict the output of something (the 'dependent' variable) based upon an input (the 'independent' variable(s)).

Where only two variables are considered (i.e. one independent and one dependent) then a *simple linear regression* can be performed. The dependent variable (designated y) is predicted from the value of the independent variable (designated x). Let us consider a practical example. Imagine that we have two columns of data: the time taken to compile a house design (hours); and the size of the house designed (gross floor area M^2). By applying a simple linear regression to these data an equation will ensue of the form:

$$y' = c + c_1(x)$$

where: y' is the predicted design time; c is a constant; c_1 is the regression coefficient; and (x) is the floor area. That is, we may employ this equation and insert any value of x to predict design time (y').

Obviously, the biggest drawback of this technique is that only one independent variable is considered. In most real-life situations there are a multitude of factors impacting on an outcome. For the above example these factors might include: experience of the designer; complexity of the design; detail required in the design; and so on. In such instances a *multiple regression equation* (MR) may be employed. This allows the researcher to measure all of these independent variables (designated x_1, $x_2, ... x_n$) and use this input data to (more realistically) predict y'. So our equation will now be of the form:

$$y' = c + c_1(x_1) + c_2(x_2) + ... + c_n(x_n)$$

where: y' is estimated design time; c is a constant; c_n are regression coefficients; and x_n are the independent variables. A few points to consider when employing regression techniques are:

O   the reliability of an MR equation will only be as good as the reliability of the input data from which it was derived; and

O   the existence of outliers (refer data exploration earlier) in input data can have a marked negative effect on reliability of the derived equation also.

Where MR is to be employed then *simultaneous regression* will consider all independent variables at the same time to build the equation. *Stepwise regression* will add one independent variable at a time to the equation starting with the 'best' predictor first, then the next best and so on. The latter technique can be useful where a large number of independent variables are to be considered and the researcher is attempting to identify those which are most significant. An example of applying MR in this context may be observed in Holt (1995 pp 301-305).

Multivariate statistics

So far, the statistical techniques discussed have considered one dependent variable. Multivariate techniques (as they are known) also exist and are able to consider several dependent variables in tandem with several independent variables. These methods are much more complex in nature and beyond the scope of this book. However, if a multivariate situation exists in your research in the first instance you may wish to investigate *Multivariate Analysis of Variance* (MANOVA) and *Multivariate Discriminant Analysis*.

Presentation of the research findings

In an abstract sense, this entire book deals with textual presentation (the beginning, the middle, the end), with chapter two being particularly specific in this objective. Therefore, the following section deals primarily with presentation of Figures and Tables. As a student you should be mindful that good presentation is essentially a function of consistency, and logic. Consistency calls for a predetermined set of presentation criteria for Tables and Figures (e.g. with respect to titles and underlining) and, keeping to those criteria. Logic means presenting things in a most understandable manner and, in such a way as to avoid potential ambiguity. That is, will the reader understand <u>exactly</u> what message is being conveyed or could the message be perceived differently? If the latter is true then ambiguity exists and the message needs clarification.

> TIP: Figures and Tables should be used to clearly communicate (possibly complex) information more effectively.

Obviously, with any dissertation there will be a limit regarding maximum number of words; so everything that is written must provide some (additional) contribution to the overall message. This is a feature of good writing in any situation, therefore:

O   An entire dissertation must use text and other contributory forms of communication in an effective manner. This means;

O   'other' contributory forms should not repeat what has already been presented in the text, but rather, complement the text; and

O   other contributory forms will be either Tables or Figures.

References, appendices, the glossary etc. also contribute to the meaning of the main text but these are at the end of and separate from, the main text, in contrast to being within it (see chapter four later). A Table may be considered as something that conveys 'columns' of information. This may be textual or numerical (the latter is more typical). A Figure may be regarded as anything that conveys information but is not necessarily a Table.

In either case, at this stage the following format is recommended: each Table and Figure should have a unique number, then, on the line below, a unique title. A double rule then separates this information from the main body of the Table like so:

Table X.X.
Title of the Table or Figure in bold here, note no full stop

The double rule not only separates the Table from adjacent text, but also allows Table headings to be inserted below it, like this:

Table X.X.
Title of the Table or Figure in bold here, note no full stop

Heading 1	Heading 2	Heading 3	Heading n
Column 1	Column 2	Column 3	Column n

Notice that the bottom row of Tables and Figures are also double ruled. This clearly defines where they finish. Below this double rule can be placed any footnotes or explanatory text to the Table or Figure, like this:

This is	the bottom	row of	the table

†*Footnote to the table: item one.*

The additional information is given in italics to distinguish it from the main text and remove potential for confusion. It is imperative that Tables convey additional information to that already given in the narrative; they should not just regurgitate it in tabular form. Where possible, fractions of the whole should be expressed in percentages as well as in real numbers. Table 3.3. shows how to arrange headings and sub-headings, along with most other characteristics described above.

Table 3. 3. Typical Table showing title, headings, subheadings, footnotes, percentages and real numbers for questionnaire analysis

Sample sub groups[a]	Number sent	Number[b] returned	Percentage[c] of sample
Architects	50	38 (76 %)	21 .0 %
Quantity surveyors	48	20 (42 %)	11 .0 %
Building surveyors	27	17 (63 %)	9 .4 %
Contractors	40	35 (87 %)	19 .4 %
Civil engineers	60	50 (83 %)	28 .0 %
Clients	35	20 (57 %)	11 .0 %
TOTALS	260	180	100.0 %[d]

a   *See appendices C to D for sample of respective questionnaires*
b   *Number of questionnaires duly completed from each sub-group*
c   *Percentages of total sample (180)*
d   *0.2% error due to rounding*

The most simple type of Figure is a pictograph (also known as a pictogram). These use pictorial symbols (icons) to represent numbers or statistics. They can help reinforce information given in a textual form by presenting salient points graphically. For example, consider the following statement: *For the period 1990 to 1993 inclusive, the value of new housing stock built in both UK public and private sectors, has increased year on year except for 1991.* This rather 'dry' statement could be livened-up and its message conveyed with greater strength if it was succeeded by; *-refer to Figure 3.1.* The pictograph conveys a graphical message but note from Figure 3.1. that it is not entirely accurate in terms of numeric content or inference. Where detail is important then a different form of presentation such as a Table, would be more appropriate.

Another useful, simple Figure is the pie chart; to show proportions, real numbers, percentages, or any combination thereof in two-dimensional, three-dimensional or 'exploded' form -see Figure 3.2.

Bar charts (histograms) use vertical or horizontal columns to convey numeric or comparative information, or frequency distributions. Horizontal bar charts are also useful to illustrate combined positive and negative data - see Figure 3.3. It is important that the scales of bar charts (indeed any chart) are carefully designed. If the scale is too small then detail may be lost, whereas too large a scale may mean that you have difficulty in fitting the chart onto one page!

Another type of Figure is the scatter diagram. Consider the following data which have been obtained from the results of performing a loading test on a composite plastic sample:

Load (KN.):		Deflection (mm x 10^{-2}):	
	10		3
	15		4
	20		5
	25		7
	30		9
	35		12
	40		18
	45		Fail

Figure 3.4. shows this data plotted on a scatter diagram.

Figure 3.1. UK houses built by total value 1990 - 1993

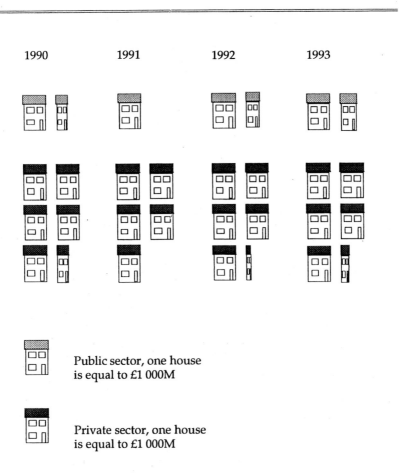

Public sector, one house
is equal to £1 000M

Private sector, one house
is equal to £1 000M

Figure 3. 2. Typical pie charts

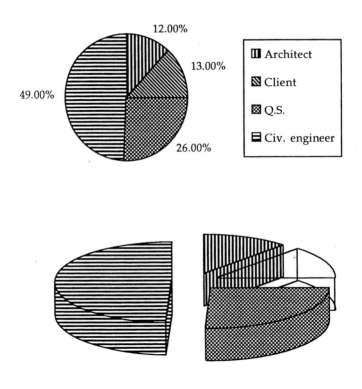

The uppermost pie chart is two dimensional with percentages shown.
The lower chart is three dimensional and 'exploded' with no percentages shown.

Figure 3.3. Simple bar chart exhibiting positive and negative data

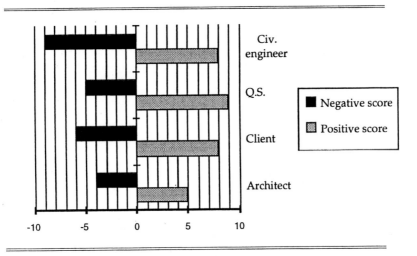

Figure 3.4. Scattergram of load versus deflection

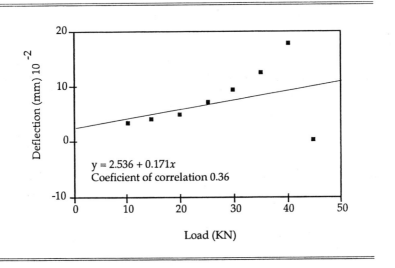

Summary of the second component: the middle

- ❏ The middle component of a dissertation describes the 'nuts and bolts' of a research: what was done, why it was done in a certain way, and the results obtained.

- ❏ A logical format for the middle is: explanation of methodology employed; description of the research (e.g. survey or experiment); details of the analysis; and presentation of results obtained.

- ❏ The fundamental research methodology employed is a function of (amongst other things): industrial or academic bias; conceptual or empirical requirements; qualitative or quantitative bias; and pure or applied bias of the research.

- ❏ Samples are usually randomly drawn from a population based on fundamental rules of sample design. In general, the more variability within a population the larger the sample needs to be and vice-versa.

- ❏ Tests may be performed, or observations (trends) noted on a sample, to determine (with a predetermined degree of confidence) certain characteristics about the population from which the sample was drawn.

- ❏ Research data analysis requires a fundamental grasp of statistics. An understanding of the nature of the research data is first required, followed by correct analyses upon, or amongst it.

- ❏ Presentation of the research findings is essentially a function of logic and consistency. Text should be complemented with correctly formatted Tables and Figures to convey salient aspects of the research (in particular the results of data analysis). They should help to make the text more interesting.

- ❏ Tables and Figures should add to the overall message of the dissertation not simply regurgitate the text in a different format.

Chapter four
Third component: The end

This chapter explains the following:

- ❏ the importance of abstracting conclusions from your work
- ❏ the importance of giving logical recommendations
- ❏ how to present bibliographic listings
- ❏ when and how to use appendices
- ❏ when and how to use a glossary

If your research has opened the door, if only by a small amount, then it will enable others to see what may be found beyond. In that respect, it would have achieved something. (Anon).

Introduction

Chapter two explained the importance of a lucid introduction to a dissertation (or any written piece of work for that matter). Such an introduction 'sets the scene' and explains to the reader, what is about to unfold. Similarly, an accomplished dissertation must end in a clear and concise manner. A lucid ending neatly reminds the reader of what has gone before and emphasises the main characteristics of the work (i.e. conclusions and recommendations).

However, defining the end is not easy. As Meloy (1994) states, this is because: "we are never, in an absolute sense, quite there". That is, a properly executed research dissertation will identify en-route to the end, several other avenues that justify further investigation. These avenues are normally grouped under the heading of 'Further work' (see later).

> TIP: The end component of a dissertation is as important as the introduction.

Despite these difficulties, the end is an important component and worthy of detailed attention. It will normally consist of three principal sections, namely:

O conclusions;

O recommendations (possibly also including indications for further work); and

O other complementary information such as bibliographic listings, a glossary, and appendices.

Conclusions and recommendations are intrinsically linked, so we will discuss them in tandem.

Abstracting meaningful conclusions and recommendations

Throughout, this book has attempted to 'labour' the point that the hallmark of good academic endeavour is originality. At first degree level this need only be a small component of the dissertation, but some originality should be there. Originality should be more evident at Masters level and in the case of a PhD, be extended to a clearly identifiable contribution to knowledge. Originality can emanate from several sources. For example, investigation of opinion, recording of process observation, or the results of experiment or survey.

Chapter three explained the importance of properly presenting findings that result from original investigation. However, the underlying ambition in all forms of research must be to draw realistic, tangible conclusions from these results.

> TIP: An underlying ambition of all dissertations should be to draw sound conclusions from the research undertaken.

As Berenson and Colton (1971) pointed out, every researcher <u>must</u> draw conclusions from their research even if they are not the ones originally sought. This means that 'negative' results are as important as 'positive' ones. Indeed, negative results may be of tremendous value and can be a legitimate contribution to knowledge. Rigorous conclusions are a feature of research that has been well designed, well executed and properly interpreted. Poor conclusions signal a research programme that has been conducted in a reactive, hasty manner, with little synthesis and a lack of direction.

Well abstracted conclusions will by definition, yield recommendations and possibly indicators for further work (research). Considered in general terms, a dissertation's conclusions and recommendations represent the 'validity' of the research reported in it. They should identify:

O   what the research has achieved;
O   what has been learned; and
O   who might benefit from the findings.

The concept of validity is worth further consideration. A particular research programme may have contributed little to the population as a whole, but taught an individual a great deal. Conversely, research might have generated tremendous benefit or interest to the population. For example, Marie Curie's original account of radioactivity had tremendous impact (Preece, 1994 chapter one) but, other than the obvious practical ramifications who is to say Marie Curie's research is more 'valid' than another? Validity is a subjective interpretation and purely relative. Nonetheless, there is a school of thought that believes in the need for 'social value' to be attached to all research particularly, that conducted at Doctoral level (see Sharp and Howard, 1996 p39). This value can be measured by:

O   contribution to academic knowledge;
O   social utility value;
O   value to the community; and
O   wealth creation potential.

Whatever your standpoint, it should be accepted that there is questionable validity in researching an 'irrelevant' topic when a more 'practical' one is available.

The former concepts reflect validity at a macro level. At micro level we may consider the validity of a dissertation in terms of its conclusions and recommendations. Do not underestimate the importance of conclusions and recommendations, or, the effort required to properly compile them. They represent a student's ability to consolidate a large volume of work into a few, well written pages. This means that the length of time taken to complete this section of a dissertation is great when compared to the volume of work produced. This time factor should be recognised and adequately allowed for.

Conclusions

Within any built environment dissertation the heading *Conclusions*, should signal that the following section will present, in a succinct format, the logical outcome of all that has gone before (Turk and Kirkman, 1982). O'Connor (1995) suggests that conclusions should state the significance of results, briefly. They should not claim too much, nor, hedge your claims unduly.

The biggest single mistake that can be made by students in this respect is not to properly understand what has been done during the dissertation period. That is, the failure to properly draw any conclusions from the work. The most recurring mistakes are abstraction of wrong conclusions from the research and / or the abstraction of conclusions that simply do not exist. These mistakes are best explained by hypothetical example.

Let us assume that a first degree dissertation student has surveyed opinion of the learning requirements for undergraduates of Building Management, amongst senior managers of contracting organisations. The student has presented the following conclusions:

1.   *The response rate from the survey was very high at 73 per cent. Overall, the outcome of the survey was as expected.*

2.   *The three most important learning requirements for undergraduate students are: an ability to read drawings; an ability to communicate effectively; and an ability to understand the contractual implications of standard forms of contract.*

3.   *Contractors perceive current higher educational learning outcomes for undergraduates as being adequate.*

4.   *There is significant difference of opinion between contractors, with respect to the ability of building management graduates.*

In many ways these conclusions are wrong, either because they draw inferences that are not in the output data or, because they require clarification. Let us investigate each conclusion in turn:

1.   *The response rate from the survey was very high at 73 per cent. Overall, the outcome of the survey was as expected.*

Comment:
a)   This is not a conclusion. It is a statement that merely reports what has happened.
b)   The second sentence tells the reader nothing other than the student's opinion. What was expected anyway?

2.   *The three most important learning requirements for undergraduate students are: an ability to read drawings; an ability to communicate effectively; and an ability to understand the contractual implications of standard forms of contract.*

Comment:

a) The 'three most important learning requirements' according to who? Is this the opinion of managers, undergraduates, or the author? This requires qualification.

b) Is this for all UK 'undergraduate students', all built environment undergraduates or all undergraduates that are reading Building Management? Again, this could be better qualified.

c) For the three learning requirements cited, are they in ascending or descending order of importance or are they equally important? This conclusion would be more meaningful if this point was clarified.

d) It is assumed that the definitions of (for example) 'effective communication' were given in the questionnaire; so that all respondents were able to answer on an equal perception of their meaning. Further, these definitions should also have been explained in the write-up of the survey method in the dissertation. If this is the case then no potential for ambiguity regarding perceptions exists. Problems surrounding the elicitation and measurement of individuals' perceptions may be observed in Holt (1997).

3. *Contractors perceive current higher educational learning outcomes for undergraduates as being adequate.*

Comment:

a) Here, should 'contractors' be interpreted as 'all' UK contractors? (assuming the research was UK oriented). However, were the survey (for example) conducted in the south of England only, then this would be an incorrect inference. The conclusion should be qualified to confirm any regional or national bias. (This particular aspect should also be well documented in the description of the survey design, in the middle component of the dissertation).

b) Was the survey conducted amongst contractors of a certain size (e.g. value of turnover or number of employees), contractors of a particular nature (e.g. general contractors or specialists), or civil engineering contractors only (etc.)? This conclusion must make explicit the limitations of the findings. (Whilst discussing these points, the importance of sample and survey design now becomes apparent (refer to chapter three) i.e. the nature of the sample defines the nature and limitations of any conclusions drawn from it).

4. *There is significant difference of opinion between contractors, with respect to the ability of building management graduates.*

Comment:
a) This is a strong statement (conclusion) and requires that certain prerequisites of data collection and analysis have been satisfied to be valid. For example, how was the opinion originally measured? What statistical method was applied to test the hypothesis of different opinions? More importantly, was it the correct method? A little clarification to substantiate the conclusion, and on what basis it is being made would be better.
b) Which groups of contractors are being referred to? Difference of opinion between large and small contracting organisations or between building and civil engineering organisations? This requires qualification.

If the original conclusions are revised to take account of these criticisms, then they would probably read as follows (note that the order of presentation has been changed with the more general conclusions first, and the more specific ones later):

1. *This survey of the top 100 UK building contractors[1] has identified that the majority perceive current educational learning outcomes for Building Management undergraduates as being adequate[2].*

2. *Based on contractors' senior management for the said sample, the three most important learning requirements for Building Management undergraduates (in descending order[3]) were perceived as being: i) an*

---

[1]As defined in the(*reference here*) these being contractors based in England, Scotland, Wales and Ireland and, having a turnover in excess of £50M (Sterling 1998) per annum.
[2]This conclusion was based on a simple 'adequate / not adequate' question and majority response was 82.5 per cent.
[3]The ranking of learning outcomes was achieved by measuring opinion on a Likert scale where largest mean response = highest rank.

ability to communicate effectively; ii) an ability to read drawings; and iii) an ability to understand the contractual implications of standard forms of contract.

3. *Based on the said sample, there was significant difference of opinion between large contractors (turnover > £500M p.a.) and smaller contractors (turnover >£50M p.a. but ≤£500M p.a.) with respect to the ability of Building Management graduates[4].*

The above 'nit-picking' of the four original hypothetical conclusions may initially seem pedantic. Further, you may feel that the qualifying footnotes are a little untidy (in which case the alternative is to present this qualifying information in the conclusion itself, but I personally feel that this makes them too 'wordy'). However, the criticisms are valid observations and although somewhat contrived, <u>serve to show how easy it is to destroy conclusions</u> if a student has not adequately thought them out and presented (e.g. qualified) them properly.

> TIP: Clear, unambiguous and valid conclusions are essential. Remember that the length of time taken to compile them properly can be substantial in comparison to the volume of work produced.

Recommendations and further work

First, I will differentiate between recommendations and, further work. The Collins English Dictionary defines a recommendation as something that advises, praises or commends. If your work has identified facts that allow you to advise, praise or commend, then you should do so. You are making such recommendation based on the results of your academic endeavour. Alternatively, or in addition, your work may have identified particular areas of the subject studied

---

[4]The analysis concerned Building Managers who had graduated within the last 3 years from a University within the UK. Opinion was measured on a Likert scale and the Student's (unrelated samples) t-test was applied to the data.

that yearn for further work. In this context further work means further investigation or research.

It is apparent that the distinction between a recommendation and a suggestion for further work is somewhat blurred, particularly, when you consider that a recommendation for further work can be given!

To clarify matters, I suggest that you consider *Recommendations* as being primarily a function of applied research (refer chapter one) and inclined to 'call for an action'. Alternatively, suggested *Further work* identifies areas of the subject requiring deeper investigation; so that recommendations in their respect may ultimately be given. For the sake of readability, the following discussion uses the term 'recommendations' but the advice given equally applies to 'further work'.

Recommendations should be clear-cut and succinct. If the conclusions to your work (earlier) are correct, properly presented and adequately explained, then the subsequent step of giving recommendations is an easy one. Get your conclusions wrong, or present them incorrectly, then not only will the formulation of recommendations be more difficult, but more importantly, they will probably be wrong as well. To give an example, consider the revised conclusion number two from above:

Based on contractors' senior management for the said sample, the three most important learning requirements for Building Management undergraduates (in descending order) were perceived as being: i) an ability to communicate effectively; ii) an ability to read drawings; and iii) an ability to understand the contractual implications of standard forms of contract.

Then leading on from this we might recommend that further research should determine *why* contractors consider these requirements are important. Also, that Higher Educational establishments offering Building Management as an undergraduate subject might be investigated for their commitment to teaching these particular skills. A final recommendation might be that if academic Institutions are not meeting these 'demands', then the findings of this work be made known to them!

Because recommendations are usually short and to the point, it can be helpful to the reader if they are presented as a list (this can be numbered). As Turk and Kirkman (1982) suggest, recommendations are far from discursive reading; they should serve as a 'check list' enabling the reader to tick off in their mind the various issues presented thereby facilitating a mental 'sum-up' of the *overall* recommendation of the work.

TIP: The recommendations of your work should succinctly 'sum-up' what you have discovered.

If your research is well founded, well designed, properly executed and correctly analysed, then reliable conclusions and succinct recommendations may be confidently abstracted from it. But beware, the converse also applies.

In sum, conclusions and recommendations are two vital components of a good dissertation and certainly form part of my marking regime during assessment. The best way to check their robustness is by comparison with the original objective(s). That is, do the conclusions and recommendations answer the original research question? Do they prove or disprove the original hypothesis? You will recall that the link between beginning and end of a dissertation is essential. This concept was referred to as a dissertation's 'circular nature' (look back at Figure 1.3.).

References and the bibliography

The correct way to cite references within the narrative was explained in chapter two (*Referencing the discussion*). We will now observe how to properly present (list) these citations as a bibliographic knowledge-base at the end of a dissertation. First, three definitions will help avoid what in my own experience seems to cause a lot of confusion:

○ *List of references*: This is quite simply a listing of <u>all</u> references <u>cited</u> in the text. For the purposes of our discussion the listing will be placed at the back of the dissertation albeit, such lists can be presented at the end of each chapter (and hence containing only references cited in those respective chapters). Obviously, the academic rules governing the dissertation might state where references should be listed. If the choice is yours I personally think that a listing at the back is tidiest. This also avoids repetition when some of those references previously cited, are used in subsequent chapters. From the reader's standpoint, it takes a similar amount of time to turn to the back of a dissertation (to look at a reference), as it does to turn to the end of a chapter.

○ *Bibliography*: This is a thematic listing of information source materials (books, journals, video etc.), that are related to the dissertation subject and which were probably (but not necessarily) consulted during dissertation compilation. However, the items in a bibliography <u>are not</u> cited in the text (otherwise they would be included in the list of references). Where a separate bibliography is used then it normally follows-on from the list of references, but under its own heading.

> TIP: Discovery of information is a lot easier than a decade or so ago (via CDs, E-mail etc.) so it is easier to find subject related material. However, do not list copious amounts of (questionably relevant) material in your bibliography. List only that which is pertinent to the topic.

○ *References and bibliography*: This is simply a combination of both the above (as used in this book). All listings are presented in alphabetical order so that a particular (cited) reference can easily be found. Alternatively, the reader may wish to peruse the listing to identify other, relevant material.

I should mention, that some sources do define a bibliography as being that which includes all references cited in the text <u>and</u> other material selected for its relevance to the subject. However, (as stated at the outset!) this definition can cause confusion. It will remain much clearer if you consider *References, Bibliography,* and *References and bibliography* as three distinct items. Remember, your dissertation will contain <u>one only</u> of the following:

O   A list of references; OR
O   A list of references and a separate bibliography; OR
O   A list of references and bibliography combined.

Chapter two described and recommended that you use one or other of the two most popular forms of referencing: the Harvard method or the sequential numbering (otherwise known as Vancouver) method. Do not under any circumstances utilise both simultaneously!

Should the Harvard method be used then the listing of bibliographic references will be in alphabetical order. Note that the references are not numbered:

Adamson, J . . .
Clark, S . . .
Smith, A . . .

If the Vancouver method has been used then the list of references may not be in alphabetical order. Note that each reference has a unique number representing the order in which it was cited in the text:

[1] Clark, S . . .
[2] Smith, A . . .
[3] Adamson . . .

At this stage I will reinforce another point made in chapter two. Sequential numbering can be more time consuming than the Harvard method. First, this is because it takes an inordinate amount of time to cross-check each reference cited, with the bibliographic listing.

Second, if you should decide to insert an extra reference (or more) in the text at a later date, then this means that all references subsequent to the extra one will have to be renumbered. That is, if the new reference is number 11, then the original 11 becomes 12, original 12 becomes 13, and so on. Imagine the inconvenience (and time) this can cause if you have 100 plus references to change! In reality what tends to happen, is you avoid this 'trouble' and do not insert the extra reference. Subsequently the (potential) quality of the text suffers. This problem does not arise using the Harvard method.

Regardless of citation method used, each reference on the bibliographic listing should contain a minimum number of elements (items of information). Again, my own experience has shown that this is an area where students constantly fall short of the target, for example, by (say) listing only author and title. A complete description of how to list references is given in BS: 1629 (1989), see also E.L.S.E. (1978) and I.S.O. (1987). British Standard 1629 suggests the order of reference elements should be as follows:

O   the originator if known (or else use 'anon' for anonymous)
O   the year of publication (here if the Harvard system is used)
O   the title if applicable
O   material designation
O   place of production
O   the year of publication (here if the Vancouver system is used)
O   numeration e.g. volume, issue, page numbers
O   location of the item if rare.

These elements are mostly self explanatory. The following comments expand on areas of potential ambiguity.

Originator is most often the author(s). These should be presented by surname, then forename initial(s) in the same order that they appear on the document being listed. Where multiple contributors exist, such as a book with each chapter written by someone different, then one originator is preferred (possibly the editor in this example). Where three or less authors exist then each should be listed. Where more than three authors exist then the first author followed by *et al.* (Latin meaning: 'and others') will suffice. If the originator is not known then 'Anon' (anonymous) is sufficient.

The title must be reproduced exactly as it appears on the document being listed. If the original title contains an error (intentional or otherwise) then [sic] may be used to show that it is reproduced as original e.g. *How to right essays* [sic]. If no title exists then one may be 'made-up' to accurately reflect the contents of the material.

Material designation will explain what the item is and detail any additional information required to consult it. For example, VHS cassette, 35mm film or 3.5 inch diskette. The place of production should show city and name of publisher wherever possible e.g. London: Macmillan.

If only a portion or part of the item is applicable then this should be identified. For example, the relevant volume, chapter, pages, item number etc. Additional information for rare items should also be listed. In short, you should ensure that the listing provides adequate information for anyone else to identify and obtain access to that reference material, should they so desire.

A common fault with references is to over-abbreviate. Personally, I see no need for abbreviations in this context. After all, paper is relatively cheap and to abbreviate saves little space but can cause maximum irritation. For example, why abbreviate *The International Journal of Construction Site Management* to; The Int. Journ. of Const. Site Mngmt ? Abbreviations can also cause confusion, for example between edition and editor (ed or Ed). Now follows some fictional examples of how to list references properly:

Book;

Smith, J, and Jones, B. (1996). *Site Management, 2nd edition.* London: Black and White Publishers.

Book chapter;
Smith, J, and Jones, B. (1996). Psychology and the manager. *Site*

Management, 2nd edition, chapter four. London: Black and White Publishers.

OR

Smith, J, and Jones, B. (1996). Psychology and the manager IN: *Site Management, 2nd edition.* pp 76-92. London: Black and White Publishers.

Journal article (academic papers);

Smith, J., Jones, B. and White, M. (1995). A survey of site managers' opinions. *The International Journal of Construction Site Management.* Vol. 6, No. 4, pp 34-37. London: Black and White Publishers.

(The above is my preferred convention, but you should be aware of a variation on this. Journal volume number may be given in bold type, followed by the issue number in parentheses and pp might also be omitted), like so:

Smith, J., Jones, B. and White, M. (1995). A survey of site managers' opinions. *The International Journal of Construction Site Management.* **6** (4) 34-37. London: Black and White Publishers.

Conference proceedings;

Smith, J. and Jones, B. (1996). What do site managers really think? IN: Black, M, (Editor.). *Proceedings of the 56th International Conference on Construction Management,* pp 35-39, 14 -15th October, University of Somewhere, Chicago: Black Press Inc.

Unpublished material

Chapter two confirmed that references to published material are preferred. Should you use unpublished material, then this is best 'referenced' in the narrative rather than in the bibliographic listing. For example: "The use of partnering in the public sector has yet to be fully exploited" (telephone discussion between author and public sector quantity surveyor, January 1998, anonymity respected).

The Internet

Referencing Internet information requires a little explanation. Every computer on the Internet (the 'Net') has its own unique identity, as does every person using the Net (see Hahn, 1996). Once an address is known, then that source can subsequently be communicated with, or observed for information. At the time of writing, general consensus towards referencing the Net is to list the page viewed, along with the date it was viewed. The general form of a Net address is: userid@domain. 'Userid' is an acronym for Net user identification; '@' forms a logical link with the domain (i.e. userid is @ this domain . . .); and the domain specifies exactly where the user is located.

Domains themselves consist of sub-domains. The sub-domain furthest to the right is the most general and the sub-domain furthest to the left is most specific. To understand these components, first let us look at an electronic mail (E-mail) address. (Although you are unlikely to reference an individual and more likely to reference a computer serving the net, the components of each address are very similar). This is my E-mail address at the time of writing: G.D.Holt@wlv.ac.uk. G.D.Holt is my userid, and I am located (@) at (then reading the sub-domains from right to left):

uk	within the United Kingdom;
ac	at an academic institution;
wlv	this being the University of Wolverhampton.

These same concepts apply to Uniform Resource Locators (URLs). 'Earls' as they are pronounced, are locations (addresses) of computers that serve you with specific information. Hence, information referenced in a dissertation as coming from the following address can now be understood:

Anon, (1998). http://www.wlv.ac.uk/lib/systems/sebegate.htm
Viewed 6th March 1998.

The acronym 'http' stands for HyperText Transport Protocol which put simply, is the protocol used to send hypertext over the Net. 'www' stands for world wide web, which is an entry point into the Net. For greater expansion on these points see Hahn (1996) and Thomas (1996). The remaining components of the reference are similar to that explained for an E-mail address. This web page gives details of the University of Wolverhampton's internet resources, in engineering and construction related subjects.

> TIP: Regardless of the item or citation method used, references should be listed in such a way that they can easily be 'discovered' by someone else if desired.

Appendices

Having read so far into this book, you should now appreciate the importance of clear, concise writing in a dissertation. Why go to such lengths to plan, structure, edit and produce a clear piece of written work, only to clutter it up, or fragment it, by insertion of long tables, photographs and copies of completed questionnaires etc? This defeats the initial objective.

Hence, it is better if you file these complementary pieces of information in appendices. "Use appendices to clear supporting information out of the way of readers' concentration on the main theme" (Turk and Kirkman, 1982). They are normally placed directly after the references and / or bibliography at the rear of a dissertation (refer *Structure and approach* chapter one). Think of appendices as providing supporting information that is not vital to the understanding of the main text, but, is filed to offer clarification or additional information, should the reader wish to consult it.

Appendices should be clearly referred to in the narrative, so as to direct the reader like so: "A spreadsheet detailing this raw data is presented in appendix A". If more than one appendix is used then these should be given alphabetic designation (rather than numeric), using capital letters (appendix A, appendix B, appendix C etc.). Each appendix will be titled, or given its own title page briefly describing what it is, for example:

Appendix A: Survey questionnaire (private sector version)

They should be filed at the rear of the dissertation in exactly the same order that they are referred to in the narrative. Examples of appendix information include: a data base, a computer program, mathematical back-up calculations, working drawings, photographic evidence, etc. A further item might be a glossary of terms, but this can also justify a section in itself.

The glossary

A glossary is an alphabetical listing of terms or definitions. There is no real need for a glossary unless there are a substantial number of items requiring definition or, the dissertation uses an abundance of specialist (e.g. mathematical) symbols. The glossary can follow on from the appendices, or from the references / bibliography where no appendices exist. In many ways it is like an appendix because it aims to clarify (or complement) the text, but eliminates the need for interruption of the text with such definitions. Here are some examples of glossary items:

Glossary of terms

Profit before interest and tax Gross operating profit after deduction of all direct costs and overheads but before deduction of loan interest and corporate taxation.

Turnover Gross value of all sales and other income generated as a result of principal trading activities.

Capital lock-up	The difference between all capital expended on the project and all capital received from the project; at any one point in time.

Note that the definitions might not be 'universally accepted' versions (wrong definitions are not acceptable in any circumstances), but rather, they should reflect the exact meaning of the terms; as in the context of their use within the dissertation.

Glossary of symbols

A'   Complement of A relative to universe U
O_{rj} Option *r* with respect to attribute *j*
Σ The sum of
etc.

Note that within the glossary, letters should be presented in alphabetical order, even if for example, the Greek alphabet is used.

Summary of the third component: the end

❏ A good ending is as important as a good introduction in a dissertation. The end will normally contain conclusions, recommendations and other complementary material such as references and appendices.

❏ Conclusions and recommendations should identify achievements, what has been learned, and who might benefit from the work.

❏ Conclusions must be drawn accurately and reflect exactly what the work has discovered. Recommendations should be given based on the conclusions. If the conclusions are weak or incorrect, then the recommendations will be weak also.

❑ Recommendations may also include indicators for further work. Alternatively, further work may be listed separately.

❑ Recommendations generally reflect findings from applied research.

❑ Suggestions for further work generally highlights areas of the subject worthy of extra investigation.

❑ A list of references contains all material cited within the text.

❑ A bibliography lists material relevant to, but not cited, within the text.

❑ All bibliographic listings should contain adequate information, as to enable anyone else to 'discover' the item if so desired.

❑ Appendices file away complementary information that would otherwise fragment the main text.

❑ Appendices should be identified using capitalised letters and be filed at the rear of the dissertation in the same order they are referred to in the text.

❑ A glossary may be used to describe specialist terms or symbols that appear in the main text.

Chapter five
Concluding tasks and thoughts

This Chapter:

- ❑ explains how to edit your written text
- ❑ introduces some fundamental concepts of writing style
- ❑ highlights pitfalls to be avoided for achieving success
- ❑ explains how to prepare for an oral examination

A man would do nothing if he waited until he could do it so well that nobody would find fault (John Cardinal Newman, 1801-1890)

Introduction

From the preceding four chapters of this book, it is apparent that the quality of a dissertation will principally be a function of the soundness of the research and 'originality' of the work. However, sound research in itself is not enough. The dissertation narrative (I affectionately refer to this as the write-up), must be logically structured and professionally written to accurately report what was performed. This chapter offers guidance in that respect. Whilst poor research that is well written-up will not constitute a good dissertation; neither will sound research that is reported, and presented, poorly.

Editing the text and writing style

The quality of any written communication is improved the more it is revised and corrected. This is termed editing the text. Correct usage of words, phrases and punctuation are also required and these are aspects of writing style.

Editing the text

The Collins English Dictionary states that to edit, is to prepare for publication. Your dissertation might not be going into print, but such an approach in terms of preparing, or perfecting the work (for publication) is the correct way to perceive what must be done during editing. It may also be thought of as 'revising' the text. Unless you are a 'natural' with pen and paper, just about everything formal that you write will require editing to some extent. If I may cite my own work as an example; everything I write is edited at least three or four times. The method I use (and recommend you also adopt), involves the following stages:

○   write the first draft;
○   'sleep on it' (see below);
○   edit the work;
○   'sleep on it';
○   edit the work;
○   and so on, until satisfied with the text.

I call this 'sleep on it' (SOI) editing. It is an intentionally drawn-out process, which can be laborious and even painful at times! However, you need to follow the same procedure if you want your writing to be as readable and correct as possible.

SOI means this: put the earlier draft away and do not look at it, or even think about it, for several days (if time will not allow this then your planning was incorrect). A period of several weeks is even better and is yet another reason for commencing your write-up of the dissertation early in the research programme. (Refer *Planning the task*, chapter one). This process of putting the work to one side has been aptly described as 'burying the draft' (O'Connor, 1995 p74). That is, bury it in a drawer for as long as you can prior to looking at it later with a 'fresh eye'.

To understand the SOI concept, try this experiment. Take a page or two of your own recently written text, a text that you are reasonably satisfied with. Put it away for several days without looking at it. After this period of time has lapsed, read through the text in detail and you will find adjustments that need to be made. These may be minor additions (simply a comma or two) or perhaps the odd word here and there. You may even decide to add complete sentences. Conversely, you might want to make omissions. Whichever the case, the need or desire to make adjustments is evidence that SOI editing portrays the original work in a different light.

> TIP: Put early drafts of your dissertation away for several days before revising them with a 'fresh eye'. This will highlight errors or potential improvements and so improve the text.

So in the first instance, editing requires patience, persistence, and time, but how do you edit? That is, what exactly do you need to do? In short, the text must be (made) as logically structured, correct and readable as possible. This ambition may be approached in two stages. First, by analysis of writing structure. Second, by analysis of writing style. We will now look at each of these concepts in a little more detail.

Clarity and logic of structure

If the *overall* dissertation structure was established at an early stage in the research (refer *Titles and Headings*, chapter two), then logical structure of text should already be achieved in part. At this later (editing) stage, the text must now be slowly and carefully re-read (concentrate on one page at a time), with the aims of ensuring:

      O   that each individual sentence is an unambiguous

statement in itself, with a logical start and finish;

O   that each paragraph is a sensible group of sentences that collectively deal with a single issue. That is, a sentence dealing with a completely new issue, should in most cases be the start of a new paragraph. (See Figure 5.1.).

These initial aims are best shown by example. Consider the following passage of text:

The survey confirmed that contractors achieve award of contract once in approximately every five tenders submitted meaning that clients must ultimately pay for the costs expended on the remaining 80 per cent of tenders compiled. When considered jointly with the fact that open methods currently account for 20 percent of tendering arrangements it seems that clients overlook the real issues of costs i.e. open methods might encourage lower bid levels but the higher proportion of wasted resources that these methods create offset savings. Clients should reduce open tendering if the target of 30 percent reduction in real construction costs advocated by Latham are to be achieved.

This paragraph is reasonably logical but it does not separate the issues discussed from each other. Therefore, the reader needs to occasionally stop and take account of exactly what is being communicated. The text is therefore perceived as being 'long-winded' and one which creates fatigue in the reader's sub-conscious mind. Alternatively, the following passage is almost identical to the above example but, with the difference that logical sentences and paragraphs have been created. This has the effect of yielding something which is a lot easier to read:

The survey confirmed that contractors achieve contract award only once in approximately every five tenders submitted. This means that clients must ultimately pay, for the costs expended on the remaining 80 per cent of tenders compiled.

Consider this jointly, with the fact that open methods currently account for 20 per cent of all tendering arrangements, and it seems that clients are overlooking the real issues of procurement costs. That is, open methods might very well encourage lower bid levels, but the higher proportion of wasted resources that they create, offset any potential savings.

Clients should reduce open tendering, if the target of 30 per cent reduction in real construction costs advocated by Latham are to be achieved.

Figure 5.1. Aims: editing the text structure

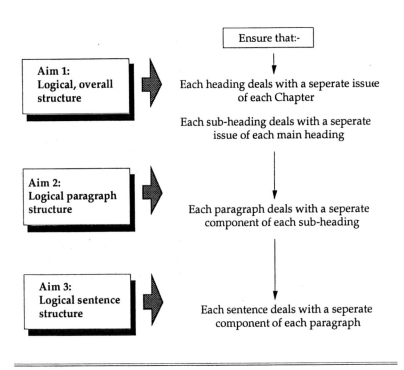

From this example you can appreciate that shorter, logical sentences avoid the 'fatigue' referred to earlier. In effect, a series of 'rests' have been created. It is more difficult to convey this message of creating 'rests' with only a short passage (I could use a much longer example but do not want to send you to sleep!). However, you can determine what is required regarding structure of the text.

Whilst discussing rests and readability, (notice the new emphasis of issue and hence new paragraph), a method exists by which to assess how easy a passage of text is to read. This is a number, known as a 'fog index'. Where a fog index is less than 20 then this represents an 'easy' to read text, whilst an index over 40 may be considered as difficult to read. Note that a low index does not automatically mean that the text is correct; it only provides an estimate of readability. To calculate a fog index, follow these four stages:

1.   Take a sample of text about 100 words long. Find the average number of words in each sentence.
2.   Ignoring words that begin with a capital letter and combinations of short, easy words (e.g. word-processor), count the number of words containing three syllables.
3.   Express the number of three syllable words as a percentage (i.e. [number of three syllable words ÷ total number of words] x 100).
4.   Add the average sentence length from (1), to the percentage from (3), to calculate the fog index.

For those who would like to know more on readability see Brewer (1994 p22), which also offers some examples of writing and respective fog indices. Incidentally, this particular paragraph has a fog index of about 29. Having discussed how to strive for optimal structure during editing, we will now investigate some aspects of writing style.

Writing style

It is not my intention to deal with style in detail. This is because any student conducting research and writing a dissertation, will not have the spare time to study this comprehensive aspect of writing science in isolation. Further, because there is a vast range of literature already available on the subject. In the first instance I would recommend Manheimer (1973); Parsons (1973 p.55 onwards); MLA (1977); Booth (1993); Sprent (1995); and O'Connor (1995). Rees (1970) explains the rules of printed English very well, whilst Kirkman (1995) deals purely with style. Turabian (1983) is extremely helpful in that it is written in a research / dissertation context. However, in the following I will discuss some of the most common mistakes made by students with respect to writing style.

First my own 'pet dislike'. It was mentioned during the introduction to this book that use of 'the first person' is best avoided in a dissertation. That is, you should write in a passive manner and avoid "I", "we", "my" etc. An impersonal text reads more 'matter of fact' and professional. Consider the following examples:

My dissertation is concerned with construction procurement. I chose this subject because it is topical and relevant to the findings of Latham. It is also of relevance to me and my employer because I work in the procurement department of a local authority. I decided to look at three particular aspects, namely: i) methods, ii) current trends; and iii) scope for change. I investigated (i) and (ii) by conducting a national questionnaire survey: my findings were most interesting! Analysis of the survey data was conducted with the help of my friend who works at the university computer department. Together we..........etc.

Notice how much more professional the impersonal version reads:

This dissertation is concerned with construction procurement. The subject is both topical and pertinent to the recent recommendations of Latham. Further, it is a subject dear to the heart of the writer, who works for a local authority procurement department. Specifically, this dissertation examines three aspects of procurement, namely:

> *i) methods;*
> *ii) current trends; and*
> *iii) scope for change.*

The first two of these aspects were investigated via a national, structured questionnaire survey of public and private sector clients. The findings of this survey were most revealing . . . etc.

The latter example has also introduced a couple of paragraphs to aid structure. Also note that if someone did assist the writer with data analysis, it would be better to mention this in the Acknowledgements. Also, beware of plagiarism!

> TIP: Avoid writing in the first person. Aim at all times to produce a 'professional' text.

Punctuation is in my experience the second most problematic area for students. The most regular mistakes are made with respect to commas, colons, semicolons, and apostrophes, so we will look at each of these individually.

Commas (,) should be adequately used to make for ease of reading by creating occasional rests. Think of their use in terms of allowing a reader to stop to draw breath! But, do not, overdo commas, or, as you can see, their presence, makes text, difficult, to read.

The colon (:) gives stronger discontinuity to text than does the semicolon (;). Hence the semicolon is in a sense subservient to the colon, like this one preceding the:

separation of listed items;
numbered or otherwise;
the last finishing with a full stop (period).

Apostrophes (') seem to cause most distress. Possession can be expressed using an apostrophe s ('s). That is, the addition of apostrophe s to a noun or name, makes it of the *possessive form*. For example:

. . . the respondent's questionnaire was incomplete.
. . . the model's integrity was confirmed.
. . . a comparison was made to Ward's data.

A plural noun or name that already ends in 's' need only have the apostrophe added to generate the possessive form:

. . . using Jones' method of analysis.

The use of an apostrophe in this way does not affect the pronunciation. Alternatively, it is also correct to add apostrophe s ('s) in the last example (e.g. Jones's) but, this does change the pronunciation to "iz" i.e. "Jonesiz" (cf. Collins, 1995 pp 102-105 and p 443).

Apostrophes can also add some meaning to what would otherwise be unintelligible text. For example: 'To consider the pro's and con's'. They may also account for the omission of part of a word e.g. pro's (professionals) or haven't (have not).

The remaining points with respect to writing style are presented as bullet-points and might be considered as a basic check list:

O Figures and Tables must be plainly separated from the text by horizontal ruled lines at the top and bottom of each. Insert at least two spaces, both above and below these lines. Many students try to cram too much onto one page. Tables should also be clearly titled and numbered in accordance with the guidelines given in chapter three.

O Check the spelling! Most word processors have spell check facilities on them (and grammatical checks also in some cases). Ensure that the spelling is correct for the given contextual situation e.g. "samples were removed form the laboratory" (the spell check will not detect form [from] as being incorrect). Use the correct UK / USA spelling as applicable; e.g. centre or center and should it be one word or two? e.g. you are now reading a *textbook,* but you look for a telephone number in a *'phone book.*

O Capitals should begin all personal names, all place names e.g. Manchester; England; America; and all institutions e.g. The Chartered Institute of Building; The University of Somewhere.

OTHERWISE, TRY TO RESIST USING CAPITALS BECAUSE AS YOU CAN SEE, UPPERCASE TEXT AS IT IS OTHERWISE KNOWN, TENDS TO MAKE READING MUCH SLOWER AND MORE DIFFICULT.

O Remember to consistently use the hierarchy of titles and headings decided upon at the outset (refer chapter two) and note, that there is no need for a full stop at the end of each. That is, **Chapter 1: Introduction** is preferable to **Chapter 1: Introduction.** You will recall from chapter three that the latter principle also applies to titles for Tables and Figures.

O One final piece of advice with respect to writing style is avoid using gender (him, her, his, hers etc.). If you apply a little thought, sentences can easily be restructured to achieve this.

TIP: Good writing is expressed simply and is easy to understand.

Pitfalls to avoid in dissertation study

Well here lies opportunity for me to write another book! The most fundamental pitfall is to mis-understand what dissertation study is all about. Reading this book will tell you most of what you need to know about researching and writing a dissertation and so should counteract that! In short, (and this is a good maxim for all study) understand what you are doing; do not simply wander aimlessly. Regarding pitfalls, the most important considerations are as follows:

O The correct choice of subject is essential. The wrong choice of subject will certainly lead to a difficult or unsuccessful dissertation experience. Read and understand the section: *Choosing a topic* (chapter one).

O An appropriate supervisor is also a prerequisite to success. Expertise in the subject area and no potential areas of student /

supervisor conflict are required. However, the best supervisor in the world is of no benefit to you if you do not communicate; liaise with your supervisor closely from the outset. Do not think that to charge ahead with the work on your own initiative and avoid liaison, will create a good impression: it will not. First, this is because your supervisor will want to play an active role throughout. Second, your biggest risk is that you may be going in totally the wrong direction with your work and when this is eventually realised, valuable time will have been wasted.

O   Adequate and realistic planning of the research and dissertation writing exercise is necessary. Very often students do not plan because they do not see it as important. Rather, they incorrectly perceive it as a worthless exercise that merely eats into precious time. Please believe me that inadequate, or no planning leads to the 'aimless wander' referred to many times over in this book.

O   Neither should a dissertation plan be put away and forgotten, otherwise it may just as well not exist. Be dynamic and take the time to chart your progress against the activities and time scales on your plan; you will then be in a position to take corrective action where necessary.

O   Do not attempt any form of plagiarism. The copying of someone else's work and putting forward such as your own is not only morally wrong, but you also run the risk of being found out. In this case you may be disqualified from your degree. Further, you should recognise that plagiarism will tarnish your personal reputation.

O   If you are using a questionnaire for data collection apply adequate thought to its design particularly, in terms of "how will I achieve a meaningful analysis of this data". Do not just ask questions for questions sake; proper understanding of your objectives and the analysis method(s) that will be applied to your data, will help in this respect. Some companies receive many requests to partake in surveys etc. and a poor questionnaire is not only a bad reflection on you and your academic institution, but also, it stands less chance of a response. Do not use (e.g. your academic institution's) headed letter paper, or somebody else's name (e.g. your supervisor's) on a questionnaire or covering letter, without permission.

O   Similar thought needs to be applied to the designing of models and experiments. "How will I analyse this output or data?" and "how can I validate this method?" are questions that should constantly be addressed.

O   Use the correct method of data analysis. For example, if testing for a significant difference between means of samples using a student's t-test; are the prerequisites of equality of variance and normality met? If not, use another method (e.g. a nonparametric test). Also, be sure that the test or analysis you are performing is appropriate for your investigation. There is nothing worse than spending precious time on an in-depth analysis only to discover that it was inappropriate for what you were trying to achieve, prove, or show, in the first place.

O   Leading on from the last item, be sure that your findings are correct. Do not draw inferences on results or outputs of analysis that are not there. Violation of statistical prerequisites or the using of a wrong test / sample / material / design etc. will mean that your inferences will be wrong. Further, such inferences will have to be qualified in some way or be of limited meaning.

O   Be conscientious about your work and the way you present it but do not fall into the trap of constantly striving for perfection. Such a research programme will never be completed. If you find that you are beginning to question or doubt your own work do not be disheartened, this is normally a positive sign. It shows that your thinking and ability to synthesise a situation or problem has advanced. However, if in doubt talk your concerns through with your supervisor.

O   <u>Time is your biggest enemy</u>. Never put off until tomorrow what you can reasonably achieve today, the days go by at an alarming rate. Never waste a moment. Too many students have to enter a final dash for the finishing line <u>unnecessarily</u>. Nothing can better spoil an otherwise potentially good piece of work.

Finally, to conclude this section on pitfalls a survey was conducted amongst 15 of my colleagues; all of whom supervise dissertation students at all levels. This survey had three aims:

1. to highlight the most common spelling / grammatical mistakes made by dissertation students;
2. to highlight the most common 'general' mistakes or failings made by dissertation students; and
3. to invite one piece of key advice for dissertation students from each supervisor surveyed.

The results of this survey are presented below and offer a valuable insight.

Most common spelling / grammatical mistakes

The survey question asked: "Based on your dissertation supervision experience, please list the five most common spelling / grammatical mistakes made by students (as one respondent confirmed: "spell checkers have all but removed spelling mistakes; it is now more a case of wrong word usage i.e. grammatical errors). Write the most common mistake at the top of the list, then continue in descending order of occurrence".

By calculating a mean ranking from the survey response (that is, the smallest sum of ranks = most frequently occurring mistake), the following results were uncovered:

Rank	*Word*	*Incorrect spelling / usage*
1.	There	Their (and vice-versa)
2.	Too	To
3.	Where	Were
4.	Know	Now
5.	Effect	Affect
6.	Could have	Could of
7.	Lintel	Lintol
8.	Sceptic	Septic (tank)
9.	Dissertation	Dissatation (!!)
10.	Company's (possessive)	Companies (plural).

Two others that frequently arise in my experience are:

1. Principle (fundamental truth or basis of reasoning); and
    Principal (primary, main, or leading, point / issue etc.).
2. Its (possessive, of itself); and
    It's (it has, it is).

Most common 'general' mistakes / failings

These were also ranked in a similar way to that described above. The survey asked: "Based on your dissertation supervision experience, please list the five most common mistakes / failings made by students that impede on their final dissertation grade". The results were as follows:

Rank	*Mistake / failing*
1.	Poor planning and organisation
2.	Poor time management
3.	Failure to liaise closely with the supervisor
4.	Poor presentation
5.	Poor literature search
6.	Aims / objectives inadequately thought out and stated
7.	Lack of checking (e.g. editing)

8.   Poor questionnaire design

9.   Emphasis on volume; not quality

10.   Poor conclusion.

Key advice

This question asked: "Given the opportunity to offer students one piece of advice with respect to achieving successful dissertation study (i.e. an enjoyable experience for the student and achievement of a good grade), what would that one piece of advice be?". The most interesting responses in no particular order were:

"Plan carefully at the start. Use the plan throughout your study to monitor progress and in discussions with your supervisor".

"Choose a topic of genuine interest, i.e. one that will motivate and stimulate your efforts. Then, decide on a set of objectives that will enable you to satisfy your goal".

"Choose a topic that is of genuine interest to you; otherwise the task will become a chore".

"Establish clear objectives with an associated research methodology having some rigour in it".

"Produce a realistic time managed plan, agree this with the supervisor and stick to it".

"Take time over your synopsis. Firm up your proposal with your supervisor, be clear as to your objectives and stick to them. Avoid thinking that quantity of output directly relates to quality; it doesn't".

"Start developing the right attitude; you will soon be a graduate (in the case of first degree students) and your employer will expect you to be capable of writing professional reports on each assignment given to you".

"Write the conclusion before you start! That is, think about what the conclusions should state and plan your work to achieve that. Obviously precise details will not be known until the end, but, such consideration at an early stage will focus the dissertation".

The remaining pieces of advice all emphasised the importance of choosing a suitable topic.

To summarise, a student who falls into any of the pitfalls identified in this section will almost certainly experience problems; and hence, find the dissertation experience a difficult one. In the alternative, if you avoid the problems outlined above then the task will be easier. That way, you can also enjoy your dissertation study and look back on it in a positive light, not as a nightmarish event!

The oral examination

A viva-voce is an oral examination. Obviously, because a dissertation is a study of one specific topic, no (written) exam paper will be available for it: hence the viva-voce. Albeit some (undergraduate and postgraduate) dissertations will require a successful viva-voce prior to the award being conferred on a student, oral examinations are primarily associated with higher degrees undertaken by way of research, such as the MPhil or PhD.

The discussion (yes it is a discussion not an interrogation!) that takes place in a viva-voce will revolve around the general area of science surrounding the topic. It is unlikely to deal *solely* with the specific aspect studied. Likewise, it may be formal or informal. The most formal scenario involves a student sitting before a panel (one or more external examiner(s) and the internal supervisor), then having to discuss the points / questions raised by the panel in a (hopefully!) learned manner. Conversely, an informal examination may simply be a discussion about the completed dissertation, between the student and internal supervisor(s). Obviously, a formal viva-voce will require much more planning and preparation, than will an informal viva-voce.

It is difficult to predict the exact format that a viva-voce will take. In many ways this will be a function of the intentions, character and concerns of the examiner(s). However, it is possible to list the main purposes of such an exam and hence, the student may gain an insight as to what might be a typical sequence of events. The main purposes of a viva-voce are:

O   The examiner(s) need to confirm the authenticity of the work. Obviously, a student who has plagiarised information without really understanding it, will find it much more difficult to have an informed talk about the subject.

O   In achieving the above, the examiners are also testing the student's knowledge and professionalism of the specific subject and, of peripheral subject issues. Particularly in the case of higher degrees, the student should have become expert in the field of study as a direct result of pursuing the dissertation. This expertise and professionalism will be sought: so show it!

O   If well written, a dissertation will not only elicit the research findings but also indicate exactly how the research was conducted. Even so, there are limitations as to the extent of such explanation in a written document. Therefore, the examiner(s) will most likely want further detailed description of what the student undertook and exactly how this was done.

O   The examiner(s) may have areas of doubt with regard to (say) methodology, or inferences drawn by a student. These concerns will need to be satisfied in the examiner's mind. This is important because at the beginning of a viva-voce, the examiner(s) will most probably have an open mind regarding such. It is up to you to confirm that what you did or inferred was correct. Failure to do so is one of the possible reasons that a student might fail the viva-voce.

O   The examiner(s) will prcbably be well versed or expert in the dissertation subject (by virtue of being the chosen examiner!). A viva-voce provides opportunity for the examiner(s) to expand on this knowledge base and hence, can in fact be a learning experience for them also. I personally know of one particular instance where a PhD viva-voce went on for nearly a full day, for this specific reason.

O   The viva-voce is an opportunity for feedback to be offered to the student.

I cannot offer a definitive method of revising or preparing for the oral examination. In view that we are all individuals I do not think one exists. However, a range of common sense actions may be taken in preparation. Again, the following may be regarded as a check list:

O   There is no substitute for thorough preparation. To achieve an air of confidence and be adequately competent in the topic, will require almost as much effort as writing the dissertation itself. Firstly, re-read the dissertation: this is particularly important for work that has been carried out over a long time period. The student must be familiar with what was performed and investigated, even during the very early stages of the research programme.

O   When reading your dissertation always have a pen and paper at hand. Constantly look for points of note or areas of contention that the examiners may pick up on. Learn how to answer these potential areas of questioning. Better still, learn how to do so quoting refereed or published material; in order to more reliably substantiate your standpoint.

O   Ask someone not associated with the project or subject to read your finished work and conduct an informal 'question and answer' session. This is not only good practice for the real thing but may also reveal ambiguity, bad writing, lack of logic etc.

O   If you have friends or colleagues who have been through the viva-voce process (particularly at PhD level) then talk to them and try to develop a feel for what the oral exam is all about. Doing this can help to prepare mentally for the 'big day'.

O   Perhaps most importantly: learn how to summarise the entire dissertation and, be able to quote this summary in about ten to 15 minutes if requested to do so. This is because nearly all vivas commence with the line: "So can you tell us (me) what you have been doing and what your dissertation has achieved (or contributed to knowledge)?"

O   Is there recently published material relevant to your topic? For example, literature on your subject that has been published since your dissertation was completed. You must keep up to date with advances or changes regarding your subject area.

O   Do not be overawed by the event. Approach the viva-voce in a calm, confident, and relaxed fashion. A student who is not confident (with the subject) will be on-edge, nervous, and want to rush the experience. The examiner would much rather confer the award on someone who is calm and confident. If you are a nervous person then begin to prepare for the viva early, perhaps a 'mock' viva will help in this respect also?

O   During the examination, pay full attention to the examiner speaking to you. Be sure to listen to the questions asked and if you do not understand a question, ask for it to be clarified (it is better to do this than try and guess what the examiner meant). Always answer the *specific* question put to you. Do not as an alternative, go off on a completely different tangent: to do so may be perceived as your trying to dodge an issue, or not being able to answer a point raised. If this is the case, then trying to avoid it can be fatal, the examiner(s) may pick up on your apparent 'weakness' and ask even more probing questions!

O   Be an expert: you are the one who performed the research and so you should be learned in your subject area.

O   It is worth remembering that few students fail a viva-voce other than those who make a mammoth foul-up. In many circumstances examiners have to complete a pro-forma document giving feedback to the student's supervisor with respect to suitability of the candidate for the award, *prior to the viva-voce*. If these comments were particularly negative then the viva-voce would not take place. Neither would the external examiner(s) waste their time attending such an examination. So remember, if the examiner(s) are prepared to give you a viva-voce then this means that they think you are capable of passing it.

O   <u>The rest is up to you!</u>

Summary of concluding tasks and thoughts

❑   Assume that your dissertation will require editing several times. Allow the time and find the patience to do this *adequately*.

❑   Approach editing in two stages: analysis of writing structure (chapters, headings, paragraphs, sentences); and analysis of writing style.

❑   Writing skills improve with practice. If you find writing difficult at present remember that practice makes perfect, so do not give up and do not ignore the merits of frequent editing.

❑   Be aware of, and hence avoid, the pitfalls that await all students pursuing dissertation study. Adequate planning and effective technique will make the task easier and subsequently more enjoyable.

❑   Understand the ethos of a viva-voce if you have to sit one. Prepare adequately and be confident with your subject.

❑   Remember that to be given an oral exam means the examiner(s) believe you are capable of passing!

Chapter six
Summary of tips

This Chapter:

❑ provides a summary of all tips provided throughout the preceding five chapters of this book

---

This short chapter provides a list of all the tips given in this book, in the order that they appear. Whilst not purporting to cover all aspects of dissertation study, this does at least provide 'food for thought'.

"Our chief interest in the past is as a guide to the future" (W. R. Inge).

○ A good dissertation has clearly communicated objective(s) (page 3).

○ Be effective in what you do. Very often, to be efficient is not in itself enough (page 4).

○ Learn to speed-read in order that you can scan large volumes of text quickly. Only relevant items of text need to be read slowly (page 6).

○ Good academic work (particularly that which is research based) exhibits a high content of originality (page 15).

○ The appropriate choice of subject is a prerequisite to successful dissertations (page 17).

○ Discuss your proposals with your supervisor at an early stage. If the proposals are flawed you can then be advised accordingly (page 19).

○ Remember that your dissertation can play a significant role in your present and future employment prospects (page 21).

○ Successful dissertations rely in part, on a good student / supervisor relationship (page 21).

○ Your dissertation stands a better chance of being successful if you identify and work to the rules governing it (page 24).

○ Compile a plan of work for your dissertation and monitor your progress. Take corrective action where necessary (page 25).

○ Begin writing your dissertation as soon as your topic is selected and your thinking on the subject has begun (page 27).

○ Try and establish your dissertation structure early on. Even if this structure is prone to changes it will still give your work some direction (page 32).

○ Always back-up your work and keep the master and back-up disks in safe, separate places (page 37).

○ You can develop a provisional dissertation structure, select a suitable hierarchy of titles and number all headings in one exercise. That way, you will develop a logical framework around which to write the main text. A typical framework is shown in Appendix A (page 43).

○ If you format your chapters as a template i.e. margins, headers, font, spacing etc. then consistency will be achieved throughout the dissertation (page 46).

○ Use the introduction to 'invite your reader in' and explain the intended route of your dissertation (page 53).

O Become familiar with your academic library as soon as possible in your dissertation studies. Learn to utilise fully, all of the resources offered (page 58).

O Careful logging of the literature and its safe storage can be time consuming, but will pay dividends later (page 63).

O Be sure to compile a micro-plan around which to write your literature review (page 68).

O Clearly identify your objectives in the introductory chapters so that the reader understands where you are going with the work (page 76).

O Choose a research methodology that will satisfy your objectives and fit into the overall framework of your dissertation. Don't choose a methodology *then* mould your dissertation around it (page 81).

O Choose a methodology commensurate with the level of degree being studied (page 82).

O When deciding on a suitable research methodology consider what tools (e.g. software) are available to analyse your data (page 86).

O The rigorous use of an appropriate research methodology is a characteristic of successful dissertations (page 90).

O Ensure your research sample is well designed in terms of stratification and size (page 94).

O Be aware that physical experimentation requires meticulous planning, accurate recording of data and can be more time consuming than might at first be realised (page 99).

O Analysis requires that you have a fundamental grasp of statistics. Limit your analysis to suit your abilities (page 100).

O Understand the nature of your data before attempting particular statistical tests upon it (page 102).

○ Figures and tables should be used to clearly communicate (possibly complex) information more effectively (page 111).

○ The end component of a dissertation is as important as the introduction (page 120).

○ An underlying ambition of all dissertations should be to draw sound conclusions from the research undertaken (page 121).

○ Clear, unambiguous and valid conclusions are essential. Remember that the length of time taken to compile them properly can be substantial in comparison to the volume of work produced (page 126).

○ The recommendations of your work should succinctly 'sum-up' what you have discovered (page 128).

○ Discovery of information is a lot easier than a decade or so ago (via CDs, E-mail etc.) so it is easier to find subject related material. However, do not list copious amounts of (questionably relevant) material in your bibliography. List only that which is pertinent to the topic (page 129).

○ Regardless of the item or method of citation used, references should be listed in such a way that they can easily be 'discovered' by someone else if desired (page 135).

○ Put early drafts of the dissertation away for several days before revising them with a 'fresh eye'. This will highlight errors or potential improvements and so improve the text (page 141).

○ Avoid writing in the first person. Aim at all times to produce a 'professional' text (page 146).

○ Good writing is expressed simply and is easy to understand (page 148).

References and bibliography

Adamson, A. (1977). A student's guide for projects and field studies. Management monograph No. 1. Thames Valley Regional Management Centre.

Anon (1984). Researcher student and supervisor-an approach to good supervisory practice. Newsletter, No. 21, Summer issue. Loughborough University of Technology, Loughborough, Leicester, UK

Anon (1995a). Construction project guide 1995-1996. Guidance and regulations for students on all construction awards taking the honours dissertation module. Internal document. Construction Division, University of Wolverhampton, UK.

Anon (1995b). The University of Wolverhampton regulations for the award of the University's degrees of MPhil and PhD. Internal document, Research Support Unit, University of Wolverhampton, UK.

ASLIB (1994). Index to theses accepted for higher degrees by the Universities of Great Britain, Ireland and the Council for National Academic Awards. London: ASLIB. Produced annually.

Avery, T.E. (1978). Student's guide to thesis research. Minneapolis: Burges Publishing Company.

Bailey, A. (1993). All write! Effective writing for professional people. Reading: The College of Estate Management.

Barbour (1996). Barbour Index Building Microfile Technical. Pub: Barbour Index plc.

Barrass, R. (1978). Scientists must write. A guide to better writing for scientists, engineers and students. London: Chapman and Hall.

B.E.C. (1996). Construction trends survey. January 1996. London: Building Employers Confederation.

Berenson, C. and Colton, R. (1971). Research and report writing for business and economics. New York: Random House.

Berry, R. (1966). How to write a research paper. London: Pergamon Press.

Berry, R. (1994). The research project. How to write it. London: Routledge.

Booth, V. (1993). Communicating in science: writing a scientific paper and speaking at scientific meetings. Cambridge: Cambridge University Press.

Bosworth, D.P. (1995). Citing your references: a guide for authors of journal articles and students. North Yorks.: Underhill Press.

Brewer, R. (1994). Write it right: a guide for preparing technical information. Building Research Establishment Occasional paper. September. Herts: B.R.E.

Brinkworth, B. J. (1973) An Introduction to Experimentation (2nd Ed.). The English Universities Press, London.

B.L.D.S.C. British Library Document Supply Centre. Boston Spa, Wetherby, West Yorks., LS23 7BQ.

Brown, E. and Smith, N. (1993). Get it write: the skills and practice of plain English for property people. Audio cassette. R.I.C.S. and the College of Estate Management.

B.S.I. (1972). British Standards Institution. Presentation of research and development reports. British Standard 4811 Amd. 2:1972. London: B.S.I.

B.S.I. (1974). British Standards Institution. Conversion Factors and Tables (two parts). Recommendations for references to published materials. British Standard 350:1974. London: B.S.I.

B.S.I. (1984). British Standards Institution. The preparation of British Standards for building and civil engineering. Part 2 guide to presentation. Published document PD6501:Part 2. London: B.S.I.

B.S.I. (1988). British Standards Institution. Recommendations for preparing indexes to books, periodicals and other documents. British Standard 3700:1988. London: B.S.I.

B.S.I. (1989). British Standards Institution. Recommendations for references to published materials. British Standard 1629: 1989. London:

B.S.I.

B.S.I. (1989). British Standards Institution. Copy preparation and proof correction. British Standard 5261 Pt. 3 Amd 1: 1989. London: B.S.I.

B.S.I. (1990). British Standards Institution. British Standard recommendations for the presentation of theses and dissertations. British Standard 4821:1990. London B.S.I.

B.S.I. (1994). British Standards Institution. Technical information on construction products and services. British Standard 4940:1994. London: B.S.I.

Calnan, J. (1976). One way to do research. The A-Z for those who must. London: William Heinemann Medical Books Ltd.

Collins (1990). The Collins Concise Dictionary Plus. London: Collins.

Collins (1995). Collins Cobuild English Grammar. London: Harper Collins Publishers.

Cox, D. R. (1958) Planning of Experiments. J. Wiley and Sons, London.

Davies, J.W. (1996). Communication for engineering students. Essex: Longman Group Limited.

Davinson, D. (1977). Theses and dissertations. London: Clive Bingley Ltd.

E.L.S.E. (1978). References in scientific publications. European Life Science Editors - Ciba foundation workshop 1978. Earth and Life Science Editing, No. 7, pp 18-21.

Everitt, B. (1980). Cluster analysis, 2nd Ed. Heinemann Educational Ltd. UK.

Felker, D. and Pickering, F. and Charrow, V. et al. (1981). Guidelines for document designers. Washington DC: American Institutes for research.

French, S. et al (1986). Operational research techniques. London: Edward Arnold.

Freund, J. and Simon, A. (1992). Modern elementary statistics. New Jersey: Prentice-Hall Inc.

Geary, R. (1970). Work study applied to building. Kent: Tonbridge

Printers Ltd, UK.

Gunning, R. (1968). The technique of clear writing. New York: McGraw Hill.

Hahn, H. (1996). The Internet complete reference 2nd edition. California: McGraw Hill.

Halsey, D. P. (1996) The Weathering of Sandstone, with particular reference to Buildings in the West Midlands UK. Unpublished PhD Thesis, School of Engineering and the Built Environment. University of Wolverhampton.

Hamilton, A. (1989). Writing matters. London: R.I.B.A. Publications Ltd.

Hamilton, A. (1990). Writing dissertations. London: R.I.B.A. Publications Ltd.

Hampson, L. (1994). How's your dissertation going: students share the rough with the dissert [sic]. Lancaster: Unit for innovation in higher education, Lancaster University.

Hannagan, T. J. (1986). Mastering statistics. London: Macmillan Education Ltd.

Harris, F.C. and McCaffer, R. (1989). Modern Construction management. Oxford: BSP professional books.

Hillier, F.S. (1990). Introduction to operations research. New York: McGraw Hill.

Hoffman, A. (1986). Research for writers. A and C Black.

Holmes, N. (1984). Designers guide to creating charts and diagrams. New York: Watson-Guptill Publications.

Holt, G. D. (1994). Construction research -what is the point?. Faculty of Building Journal, Winter Edition, pp 28-31. Nottingham: Faculty of Building Limited.

Holt, G. D. (1995). A model for predicting the performance of construction contractors. Unpublished PhD thesis. Construction Division, University of Wolverhampton, U.K.

Holt, G. D. (1997). Construction research questionnaires and attitude measurement: relative index or mean? International Journal of

Construction Procurement. Special edition, issues in construction management research methodologies, Vol. 3, No. 2, pp 88-96.

Howard, K. and Sharp, A. (1983). The management of a student research project. Gower Publishing Co. Ltd.

Humphries, J. (1994). Contractors' understanding of the factors which affect tendering levels of construction works. MSc dissertation, School of Construction, Engineering and Technology, University of Wolverhampton, UK.

Huth, E.J. (1990). How to write and publish papers in the medical sciences 2nd Ed. London: Williams and Wilkins.

I.S.O. (1976). International Organisation for Standardisation. Documentation -Abstracts for documentation and publication. I.S.O. 214:1976. Geneva: I.S.O. [I.S.O., case postale 56, CH-1211, Geneva 20, Switzerland].

I.S.O. (1987). International Organisation for Standardisation. Documentation-bibliographic references - content, form and structure. I.S.O. 690:1987. Geneva: I.S.O. [I.S.O., case postale 56, CH-1211, Geneva 20, Switzerland].

Kidd, J. (1989). Managing with operational research. Oxford: Phillip Allan Publishers Ltd.

Kinnear, P and Gray, C. (1994). SPSS/PC+ made simple. Hove: Lawrence Erlbaum Associates, Publishers.

Kinnear, P. and Gray, C. (1995). SPSS for windows made simple. Hove: Lawrence Erlbaum Associates, Publishers.

Kirkman, J. (1995). Good style writing for science and technology. London: E and FN Spon.

Leedy, P.L. (1989). Practical Research planning and design 4th Ed. London: Collier Macmillan.

Lemer, A.C. (1992). Construction research for the 21st Century. Building Research and Information. Vol. 20, No.1.

Littlechild, S. and Shutler, M. (1991). Operations research in management. London: Prentice Hall.

Madsen, D. (1983). Successful dissertations and theses. London: Jossey-

Bass Publishers.

Manheimer, M.L. (1973). Style manual A guide for the preparation of reports and dissertations. New York: Marcel Dekker Inc.

Meddis, R. (1984). Statistics using ranks-a unified approach. Oxford: Basil Blackwell Publisher Ltd.

Meloy, J. (1994). Writing a qualitative dissertation: understanding by doing. Hillsdale N.J.: Lawrence Erlbaum Associates.

MLA (1977). MLA Handbook for writers of research papers, theses, and dissertations. New York: Modern Language Association.

O'Connor, M. (1995). Writing successfully in science. London: E and FN Spon.

Orna, E. and Stevens, G. (1995). Managing information for research. Buckingham: Open University press.

Ott, R.L. (1993). An introduction to statistical methods and data analysis. California: Duxbury Press.

Parsons, C.J. (1973). Theses and project work. London: George Allen and Unwin Ltd.

Phillips, E. and Pugh, D. (1992). How to get a PhD. A handbook for students and their supervisors. Milton Keynes: Open University Press.

Pickford, L.J. and Smith, L.E.W. (1969). A student handbook on note taking, essay writing, special study and thesis presentation. London: Ginn and Co. Ltd.

Pilcher, R. (1992). Principles of construction management 3rd edition. Berkshire UK: McGraw Hill book company Europe.

Preece, R. (1994). Starting research-an introduction to academic research and dissertation writing. London: Pinter Publishers.

Questionnaire design manual. (1972). London: Social and community planning and research.

Rees, H. (1970). Rules of printed English. London: Darton, Longman and Todd.

Reynolds, L. and Simmonds, D. (1981). Presentation of data in science.

Lancaster: Martinus Nijhoff Publishers.

RIBA (1996). RIBA*ti* Technical Information microfile. Produced jointly by RIBA companies Ltd, Newcastle-upon-Tyne and Technical Indexes Ltd. Berks. UK.

Ruddock, L. (1995). Quantitative methods for the built environment. Vol. 1: statistical analysis. Warrington UK: White Castle press.

Rudestam, K.E. and Newton, R.R. (1992). Surviving your dissertation a comprehensive guide to structure and content. London: Sage publications.

Ryness, C.R. (1992). Marketing and communication techniques for architects. Harlow: Longman.

Sharp, A and Howard K. (1996). The management of a student research project 2nd Ed. Gower Publishing Co Ltd.

Sides, C. (1992). How to write and present technical information. Cambridge: University Press.

Sprent, P. (1995). Getting into print: a guide for scientists and technologists. London: E and FN Spon.

Swetnam, D. (1995). How to write your dissertation. A practical survival guide for students. Plymouth: How to books Ltd.

Taha, H.A. (1992). Operations research: an introduction. 5th Ed., London: Macmillan.

Thomas, B.J. (1996). The Internet for scientists and engineers 2nd edition. Oxford: Oxford University Press.

Turabian, K.L. (1983) A manual for writers of research papers, theses and dissertations. London: Heinemann Ltd.

Turk, C. and Kirkman, J. (1982). Effective writing: improving scientific, technical and business communication. London: Chapman and Hall.

Urry, S.A. (1991). An introduction to operations research: the best of everything. Harlow: Longman Scientific and Technical.

Watson, G. (1987). Writing a thesis: a guide to long essays and dissertations. London: Longman.

White, J.V. (1984). Using charts and graphs. London: R.B. Bowker Co.

Wilkes, F.M. (1989). Operations research: analysis and applications. London: McGraw Hill.

Winkler, A. and McCuen, J. (1979). Writing the research paper a handbook. New York: Harcourt Brace Jovanovich.

Wolcott, H.F. (1990). Writing up qualitative research. London: Sage.

Wood, W. G. and Martin, D. G. (1974) Experimental Method. The Athlone Press, University of London.

APPENDIX A
Specimen dissertation framework showing hierarchy of titles and numbering system

CHAPTER 1 TITLE
1.1.　**Main heading 1, chapter 1**
　　　1.1.1.　Sub-heading 1, main heading 1, chapter 1
　　　1.1.2.　Sub-heading 2, main heading 1, chapter 1
　　　　　　1.1.2.1. *Sub, sub-heading 1, subheading 2, main heading 1, Chapter 1*
1.2.　**Main heading 2, chapter 1**
　　　1.2.1.　Sub-heading 1, main heading 2, chapter 1
　　　　　　1.2.1.1. *Sub, sub-heading 1, subheading 1, main heading 2, Chapter 1*

CHAPTER 2 TITLE
2.1.　**Main heading 1, chapter 2**
　　　2.1.1.　Sub-heading 1, main heading 1, chapter 2
　　　　　　2.1.1.1. *Sub, sub-heading 1, subheading 1, main heading 1, Chapter 2*
2.2.　**Main heading 2, chapter 2**
　　　2.2.1.　Sub-heading 1, main heading 2, chapter 2
　　　2.2.2.　Sub-heading 2, main heading 2, chapter 2
　　　　　　2.2.2.1. *Sub, sub-heading 1, subheading 2, main heading 2, Chapter 2*

CHAPTER n TITLE
n.1.　**Main heading 1, chapter n**
　　　n.1.1.　Sub-heading 1, main heading 1, chapter n
　　　n.1.2.　Sub-heading 2, main heading 1, chapter n
n.2.　**Main heading 2, chapter n**
　　　n.2.1.　Sub-heading 1, main heading 2, chapter n
　　　　　　n.2.1.1. *Sub, sub-heading 1, subheading 1, main heading 2, Chapter n*

THIS IS THE TITLE WHICH
MAY TAKE UP MORE THAN ONE LINE

by (optional)

F. J. Yourname BSc (Hons) MSc MCIOB MICE

supervised by (optional)

Dr. F.J. Supervisor

A thesis submitted in partial
fulfilment of the requirements
of the University of somewhere
for the degree of
Something

Month
Year

Subject Index